'Good grie

'I'm cleaning   he
stood up.

Angus burst out laughing. 'You look like an urchin. A very appealing little urchin.' His arms slipped around her. As their lips met, Nicola trembled.

'Stop it, Angus, please,' she murmured.

Long, sensitive fingers stroked her cheek. 'Do you really want me to?'

A little breathlessly she said, 'Yes, I do.'

But the trouble was, she didn't.

Dear Reader

As Easter approaches, Mills & Boon are delighted to present you with an exciting selection of sixteen new titles. Why not take a trip to our Euromance locations—Switzerland or western Crete, where romance is celebrated in great style! Or maybe you'd care to dip into the story of a family feud or a rekindled love affair? Whatever tickles your fancy, you can always count on love being in the air with Mills & Boon!

The Editor

Frances Lloyd resides in Victoria, Australia. She has travelled extensively throughout Australia and Europe, and her love for the outback is vividly reflected in all of her pursuits—including her work as an Australian travel guide.

LORD OF
THE GLEN

BY

FRANCES LLOYD

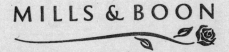

MILLS & BOON LIMITED
ETON HOUSE, 18-24 PARADISE ROAD
RICHMOND, SURREY TW9 1SR

Original edition published in 1989
by Silhouette Romances

First published in Great Britain 1994
by Mills & Boon Limited

© Frances Lloyd 1989

Australian copyright 1994
Philippine copyright 1994
This edition 1994

ISBN 0 263 78458 4

Set in Times Roman 10 on 11¼ pt.
01-9404-57669 C

Made and printed in Great Britain

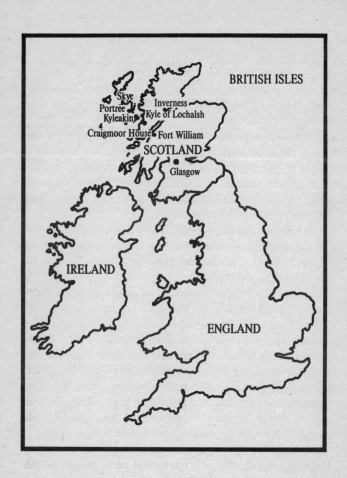

CHAPTER ONE

AT THE moment when Nicola felt sure she must be on the wrong road, help arrived. Coming towards her she saw a figure in mackintosh and rubber boots, riding an ancient bicycle. Ahead of the bicycle was a small flock of black-faced Highland sheep, who were being kept in line by a black-and-white sheepdog.

The figure dismounted as Nicola slowed and lowered the car window. A weathered face peered curiously in at her and Nicola was startled to realise that the shepherd was in fact an old woman.

"Excuse me," Nicola asked, "can you tell me if I'm on the right road for Craigie Moor?"

Penetrating blue eyes below bristling grey brows considered her with suspicion, but Nicola looked completely innocent and younger than her twenty-four years, with her clear green eyes, friendly smile and her thick brown hair that swung in natural waves about her fine-boned face. No one would guess, she hoped, that she was a journalist determined to get one of the most difficult stories of her career. And especially not Magnus Lord.

"Craigie Moor?" the old woman queried in a soft Highland drawl. "Now what would ye be wanting with Craigie Moor? It's a bleak place."

Nicola was prepared for the question. "I was told it's a good spot for bird-watching."

The ancient shepherdess's piercing blue eyes still registered suspicion. "Ach, aye," she agreed. Her narrow lips stretched into grimacing curiosity. "Ye're not a

Sassenach. Where are ye from?'' It was more an accusation than a question.

Nicola smiled. "You're right, I'm not English. I'm from Australia.''

The old woman's gaze seemed to intensify in an oddly unnerving way and she appeared not to have heard Nicola's answer. The sheep were becoming restive and the dog was circling them, herding them back against the hedge. But the shepherdess was in no hurry, and all at once her vivid blue eyes took on a strange unfocused look, as though she were looking right through Nicola or in some kind of trance. The woman began to mutter, but her accent had thickened, blurring her words so that most of what she said was incomprehensible. All Nicola could pick up were a few disjointed phrases.

"A stranger...a woman with brown hair and green eyes...she has come from across the sea...never to return, never to return.... The man desperately wants her to stay, but there are obstacles.... He is angry.... She is leaving....''

In spite of herself, Nicola felt an unnerving little tingle along her spine, a momentary sensation of being in another dimension. "What's the matter? What are you talking about?'' she interrupted edgily.

The sound of her voice seemed to rouse the old woman, and she ceased muttering. She gave a shudder and blinked, staring at Nicola for a moment as though seeing her for the first time. And then she said in a normal tone, "Australia. Aye, it's a bonny place, I've heard. The MacGregors went out there a few years back, y' ken, and young Duncan—''

"Please, what were you talking about before?'' Nicola interrupted. "You sounded as though you were seeing something. What was it all about?''

She had brown hair and green eyes. Was the old woman talking about her? Nicola had heard an unaccustomed note of panic in her voice and she tried to quell it. She was crazy to even listen to the ramblings of a weird old woman. Perhaps she would simply have scoffed and gone on her way if she hadn't had vague misgivings about her assignment somewhere deep in her bones. "What did you mean, 'never to return'?" she asked hollowly, as grim visions of accidents flashed through her brain.

The old shepherdess continued to stare at her, then said firmly, "I'm thinking ye'll be catching cold with the draught through that window, lassie, so better wind it up and be on your way. Ye're on the right road, aye, that ye are. Take the left fork a mile or two further on and ye'll soon be on the moor. Take care ye dinna get lost, lassie. There'll be a mist by nightfall and the moor's a treacherous place if ye stray off the road. There are bogs in places." For a moment she almost seemed to smile, and a faint chuckle rattled in her throat. "But I ken ye'll not need to be bothering about mists and bogs tha noo. Ye'll be safe and sound where ye ought to be." She turned away and called to the dog in Gaelic.

Where she ought to be? Nicola opened her mouth to demand another explanation, but one look at the old woman's back as she remounted her bicycle and rode purposefully away convinced her that any further questioning would be fruitless.

"Thank you for your help," she called. "Goodbye!" She closed the window and put the car into gear. As it shot forward, she glanced in the rearview mirror. The old woman, the dog and the small herd of sheep were now spread out across the narrow road. The shepherdess suddenly turned round to stare, sending a fresh prickling sensation down Nicola's spine.

"Crazy old woman," she said to herself. "I'm being fanciful. She couldn't have been talking about me." She laughed it off, but not altogether convincingly. It had been an eerie experience and she had no idea what it could all mean. Maybe if she could have understood the woman's ramblings more clearly... She glanced in the mirror again, half convinced that she must have imagined the encounter, but in the distance the tiny figures of the woman and her sheep and dog were still visible and solidly real. Nicola shrugged. "Just a crazy old woman," she muttered again, but the cryptic words the shepherdess had spoken still echoed in her mind as she drove further along the empty road.

After a couple of miles, exactly as the old woman had said she would, Nicola came to a fork. It lacked a signpost and the left branch was little more than a rutted track leading across the moor. It looked as though it was rarely used by vehicles.

What Nicola hadn't revealed to the old woman was that the moor was not her sole objective. She was looking for Craigmoor House, home of Lord Kilgarrin, better known to the film world as Magnus Lord. Magnus Lord had been one of the most inspired young cinematographers of the seventies, but for the fifteen years since the death of his wife in a boating accident, he had lived as a virtual recluse. Because some gossip columnists had said cruel things about him at the time of his wife's death, he reputedly abhorred the Press and had refused to have anything to do with journalists since that time. And his meteoric career had plunged into oblivion.

Nicola's stomach gave a lurch of nervous anticipation every time she thought of what she planned to do in order to break down his reserve and get her story. She certainly wasn't as confident as Hugh Vanter, her managing editor, that the tactic that had got her the O'Flynn story would work here. Michael O'Flynn was an Irish Australian with a wild streak and a sense of humour, and he'd appreciated her boldness. Nothing she had found in her research on Magnus Lord had led her to believe he would be as amused by her scheming. In fact, she had found out little about him at all. Despite growing fame, he had managed to hide very successfully behind his cameras, while his beautiful actress wife, Jacynth Moore, had scooped up all the limelight.

There were no roadside hedges now, only shallow ditches and frequent passing places where the narrow road widened briefly to allow vehicles to get by. It was a wild and lonely place, and Nicola encountered no one. The wind whistled shrilly around the small rented car, but bleak though it was, the countryside had a certain raw beauty, which attracted rather than repelled Nicola. The sky was a pale wintry blue, even though it was spring and low, drifting clouds made swiftly moving shadows on the landscape. There were no trees on the moor, only gorse and bog myrtle, and the stony ground was covered by a carpet of heather and grasses. In some ways its emptiness and barrenness reminded her of the parts of the Australian outback she liked the best.

The road crossed the moor in almost a straight line. Ahead loomed a range of hills. Even from a distance, Nicola could see patches of snow still lurking in shadowy ravines and on sheltered crags. Although it was warm in the car with the heating on, Nicola knew she would be glad of her padded jacket, thick sweater and tartan trousers when she ventured outside.

She caught a brief glimpse of a house a few minutes before she reached the entrance to the estate, and felt sure it was her destination. It was set in a cleft in the hills, half hidden behind a screen of skeletal trees, its sombre greyness almost merging with the bleak hillside behind it. Then for a while Nicola doubted that she really was on the right track, as the road veered away from the house.

Eventually, however, the flat, featureless moor gave way to a landscape of woods and low hills. The road twisted and turned and crossed a stream, swollen by melting snow, that foamed over a rocky bed. The wooden bridge creaked ominously as the car bounced over the planks. Nicola heard the sound of a waterfall from somewhere upstream beyond copses of alder and birch. A curlew rose abruptly from a marshy spot with high-pitched alarm calls, battled the wind briefly, then allowed itself to be swept away. It was the first bird that had captured Nicola's attention and it was a timely reminder of her cover—enthusiastic bird-watcher.

She smiled wryly to herself. Before today, what she'd known about birds could have been written on a robin's toenail but in the backpack on the seat beside her were binoculars, a field guide to British birds, a notebook and a camera with a telephoto lens. Magnus Lord was bound to discover very quickly that she was a fake, of course, but, she fervently hoped, not until she had disarmed him sufficiently for him to agree to give her a story—what he was doing now, whether he had any plans to return to film-making, and with luck, the real story of what had happened fifteen years ago.

Her job as a feature writer for *Private Lives* magazine had landed her some difficult assignments, but none as formidable as Hugh's brainchild—a series on "Whatever happened to" a number of once-famous personalities who had dropped out of the public eye during the past couple of decades.

Some of the subjects she had approached had readily agreed to be interviewed, others had required a little patient persuasion, and one or two had flatly refused to have their privacy invaded. Michael O'Flynn, a retired radical politician, had been one of the latter at first, but when Nicola, at Hugh's insistence, had got herself a job as a cook on O'Flynn's sheep station, he had finally capitulated.

Nicola had not even bothered to approach Magnus Lord in the conventional way. He had never been at ease in the public eye, had had several brushes with the Press during his marriage to Jacynth Moore and had damned them all to hell, it seemed, after her death. It wasn't worth the airmail stamp, Hugh had said, or the overseas call, to make a formal approach. It would only put him on his guard.

"But why do we have to do a story on him, anyway?" Nicola had complained. "He's not even a cameraman anymore. You tell me he's gone back to being a lord and living on the family estate in Scotland. It sounds as though his life will make very dull reading. He's not even an Australian."

Hugh had said patiently, "But his wife was. Probably our best film actress ever, or would have been, if she'd survived and matured. She was also very beautiful...."

Nicola had laughed. "Just because you had a crush on her—"

"So did practically every red-blooded male in the Western world. Her death was a tragedy, a terrible loss, and Lord was suspected of being responsible."

"Was he?"

"Who knows? He wasn't charged with murder, but some said he should have been. And he refused to say anything about the accident except that he had tried to save her. I don't suppose you remember anything about the scandal, you'd have been rather young."

"No, I don't. I've seen one or two Jacynth Moore movies on television, though. She was a delight to watch. So natural."

Then Hugh had pointed a commanding finger at Nicola. "So go to the files and do your research. Thoroughly. There's going to be a festival of her best films in a few months, on prime-time television, so a little bird told me, and I want an exclusive, inside story in *Private Lives* to coincide with it. It should boost circulation, so we'll run it over two issues if you can get a real scoop. Maybe the man's married again by now." He paused to give full emphasis to his next remark, which he underlined with a direct look at her. "You know, don't you, that Maynah will be retiring next year? And Jane is leaving to have a baby in a few months?" Nicola nodded, almost holding her breath. He went on smoothly, "Get this story, Nicola, and prove you've got what it takes to step into Jane's shoes, and next year..." He let the promise hover unsaid, but Nicola was in no doubt about what he meant.

"You mean that?" she had asked incredulously. To become assistant editor of a magazine like *Private Lives*, which had a large circulation, would be a big step up in her career. She had hardly dared imagine herself as editor.

Hugh had smiled, confident that the bait would be more than she could resist. Nicola was a good journalist with fantastic potential, but not tough enough. She needed to be goaded or tempted, and she had to learn to put everything she could into getting her story. She'd done well with Michael O'Flynn, and Hugh had a hunch she'd do even better with Magnus Lord, given some incentive. He added for good measure, "I might even ask you to marry me if you pull this one off." He was smiling, but there was more than a touch of seriousness in the promise.

To disguise her astonishment and involuntary pleasure, Nicola had scoffed, "That'll be the day." She'd been out with Hugh many times and she admired him immensely as a journalist. She sometimes thought she was perhaps more than halfway in love with the man, but she'd put a brake on her feelings because she had never set her sights so high that she expected the Modern Magazine Group's highest flier to propose to her.

He had only been joking, of course, she told herself later. Or had he? Was she underrating herself? Could she really look forward to filling Maynah Grimes's shoes, *and* to becoming Hugh Vanter's wife? He wouldn't propose to her just to reward her for getting a good story, surely. But perhaps the joke had been a way of giving her a clue to his personal feelings about her—a hint to make her think about hers for him.

Nicola had thoroughly researched her subject and had come up with a disappointingly thin file of clippings. Although there was a prodigious amount of copy available on Jacynth Moore, her husband barely rated a mention except when he had been nominated for Oscars and other prizes, of which he had won quite a few while still in his twenties. It was obvious that he was a very private person, and even in photographs he appeared as a shadowy figure in dark glasses, eclipsed by his brilliant wife. In many pictures Jacynth was escorted by her leading men, Magnus evidently preferring to avoid the limelight.

Only one article was at all revealing, and that was an interview dealing exclusively with his work. There was nothing about Magnus Lord the man, only Magnus Lord the cinematographer. The accompanying pictures were mostly stills from his films and the ones of him showed more of his camera than of his face. The one unexpected snippet Nicola did discover was that he had a deep interest in ornithology.

"That's how you get to him!" Hugh had exclaimed triumphantly, after she had confessed to having no idea how to make the approach.

"What do you mean?"

"You'd better buy yourself a field guide to Scottish birds," he had instructed patiently, "a pair of binoculars and some sensible clothing. And pack a tent, too. You, my dear Nicola, are going bird-watching."

Hugh's plan for her was simple: she was to go to the Craigmoor estate and when accosted, as she almost cer-

tainly would be, claim to be a bird-watcher who hadn't
realised she was on private property.

"Why don't I just knock at the door?" she had suggested.

Hugh had sighed. "Because you would probably be
turned away. It's the novelty of the approach that will
make it work."

"What if I end up in gaol?"

Hugh had laughed derisively. "With your looks, I
doubt it. Magnus Lord will be captivated."

The fact that the ruse might not bring her into imme-
diate contact with her quarry didn't faze Hugh. She
would profusely apologise for trespassing, he had told
her, and beg permission to wander around the estate, re-
lying on her ingenuity to somehow effect a meeting with
the owner. According to Hugh, it didn't matter that he
might see through her cover easily; with a bit of luck he
would be totally disarmed by her nerve and cleverness,
and would allow her to persuade him to give her the interview.

At least that was Hugh Vanter's scenario. It was all
very well for him, Nicola had thought a few times since
she'd left Sydney, sitting back there in his comfortable
managing editor's chair, giving orders and directing ma-
noeuvres—he didn't have to carry them out. She was not
at all sure that this was the best way to approach Magnus
Lord, but since she hadn't come up with a better idea, she
had no alternative. When she'd confided her misgivings
to Maynah, her editor had merely laughed and said, "If
Hugh says that's how you go about it, that's how you
go."

The entrance to Craigmoor House came into view quite
suddenly and was unexpectedly daunting. Massive iron
gates were supported by grey granite pillars. Across the
gates was a notice—Private Property: Trespassers Will Be
Prosecuted. A formidable high stone wall topped with

spikes and broken glass swept away from the gates in both directions to become lost in a tangle of dwarf birches, rhododendrons and brambles. Nicola surveyed the entrance with fresh misgivings. There was even barbed wire entangled in the decorative wrought-iron spikes of the padlocked gates, making them impossible to climb. If she had to find some breach in the fortifications through which she could gain entry, her trespassing was going to look rather more deliberate than accidental, she thought.

Which way? she asked herself, glancing in either direction. Both looked equally unpromising, but surely somewhere the wall must end. It couldn't surround the whole estate of several thousand acres, could it?

It was as she stood there, undecided which way to go, that she spotted a small side gate she hadn't at first noticed. It was bound to be locked, too, she thought, but nevertheless she tried it. To her astonishment, it creaked open.

"How lucky can you get?" she exclaimed aloud, astounded to find gaining entry so easy, after all. "Somebody isn't paying attention to security around here."

The wind was cold, so Nicola went back to her car and pulled on a woollen hat, tucking her unruly hair securely under it. She hoisted the lightweight nylon pack onto her back and slung her binoculars over one shoulder. She didn't feel particularly confident. Supposing she was not challenged? She shrugged. She supposed in that case she might as well make her way up to the house and humbly request permission to bird-watch, and see if Hugh's prediction proved correct. Why, Magnus Lord might even open the door to her, she thought with a grin.

Beyond the wall were thick woods and a winding driveway. Nicola walked briskly along it, mentally rehearsing how she would introduce herself and what she would say to Magnus Lord if she encountered him.

Her thoughts were rudely shattered when, with only a short, sharp, warning bark, an enormous dog crashed through the undergrowth and knocked her to the ground. Stunned by the suddenness of the attack and too winded to even gasp, Nicola sprawled on her back on the driveway. The dog mounted guard over her, barking furiously now. Nicola stared in horror at the two rows of sharp white teeth and the wild eyes only inches from her face. She ought to have anticipated guard dogs! This one looked enormous enough to be a Great Dane, but she knew as little about dogs as she did about birds.

"G-go away! Get off! Back... back... lie down..." Nicola's voice faded to a pathetic squeak. She tried every command she could think of, but the animal stood firm. If she moved only a fraction, it gave a threatening snarl.

Nicola was terrified. What on earth was she going to do? Why hadn't Hugh thought of this possibility? After a few moments, as her eyes darted desperately around for some way out of her predicament, she became aware of a man leaning against a tree a few yards away, pointing a rifle at her. He was tall, and he was wearing a brown serge jacket and jeans tucked into leather boots. A gamekeeper, she decided. Magnus Lord was bound to employ a gamekeeper.

Well, she'd wanted to be caught, hadn't she? This was where her work began. Even from a distance Nicola could feel the impact of the man's smouldering grey eyes, their expression far from amused. She swallowed hard as she took in the broad shoulders and lean body. The snug fit of his jacket hinted at a powerful physique beneath, and his boots emphasised well-developed calves. Despite his threatening attitude he was a compellingly attractive man, and in other circumstances, Nicola thought, with a certain wryness, she'd have been delighted to meet him.

"W-would you mind calling your d-dog off?" she stammered, marginally less frightened now because she was sure he wouldn't really let the animal tear her to pieces, but feeling increasingly ridiculous because she was also sure that the man was enjoying her undignified predicament.

"Rolf! Heel!" The deep, resonant tones sent tremors down Nicola's spine that had nothing to do with fear. The dog slunk back to his master's side, and the gamekeeper gave the rifle a jerk in Nicola's direction. "Get up!" He spoke more peremptorily to her than he had to the dog.

Nicola's poise was slow to return. She was dusty and dishevelled and the woollen hat had fallen off, leaving her brown hair tumbling untidily about her face. She was also uncomfortably aware that even in her rumpled state she had kindled unmistakable masculine interest in the gamekeeper's eye.

"I said, get up," he repeated. "On your feet!"

Nicola gritted her teeth and tilted her chin defiantly. If he was typical of Magnus Lord's employees, then she would need all her wits and ingenuity to get near the redoubtable laird. But he had unwittingly given her an idea.

"All right, I'm getting up," she said meekly. As she stood, she deliberately stumbled and collapsed again, pretending that her foot had given way beneath her. "Ouch!" She grabbed her ankle, tottered a few steps, then, with an expression of anguish, appealed to her captor. "I—I think I must have twisted it." She screwed up her face in imaginary pain, hoping it would fool him.

He leaned his gun against a tree and regarded her suspiciously. Nicola held her breath. After a moment he offered a hand and she allowed him to help her up. She hopped about on one foot, wincing as convincingly as she could.

"Can't you stand on it?" he demanded brusquely.

Nicola fluttered her eyelashes helplessly and feigned apology. "I—I'm afraid I can't...."

She drew in a long, deep breath. "My car's just outside the gate. If you could...if you wouldn't mind helping me to reach it, I expect I'll be able to drive...." She made this seem a very doubtful possibility indeed, and there was a suggestion of tears in her voice.

To Nicola, he still seemed sceptical, but he said, "You'd better not try—not yet, anyway. Sit down." There was genuine concern in his tone and before she could guess his intention, he'd swept her into his arms and had carried her to a fallen log. He deposited her on it quite gently and she beamed gratefully at him. Maybe his heart wasn't too hard, after all.

"It'll be all right in a minute or two. It's probably only a wrench. I'm so sorry."

He folded his arms across his broad chest. "May I ask why you are trespassing on private property?" The *r* rolled off his tongue mellifluously and Nicola found herself so entranced by his accent, she hardly paid attention to his words. It was a moment before she collected herself.

"I—I was bird-watching. I didn't think anyone would mind if I explored the woods." She pointed at her binoculars lying on the ground where they'd been flung when the dog had attacked. "W-would you mind rescuing those?"

He took a couple of strides, picked them up and examined them speculatively before handing them to her. "Are you sure that's all these are for?"

Nicola feigned indignation. "Do I look like a Peeping Tom?"

She was sure his mouth almost quirked in the beginnings of a smile, but he erased it quickly. "How did you get in?" he demanded, his eyes flicking over her as though she might have a set of burglary tools concealed somewhere.

"Through the little gate. It's not locked."

He looked surprised, but seemed to believe her. "You must have seen the notices," he pointed out. "This is private property."

Despite the hypnotic quality of his voice, Nicola managed to remember the script. "I know, but I was excited because I thought I heard a cuckoo," she offered with her most engaging smile. "It flew into these woods, and when I found the gate open, I just rushed in. One gets a bit carried away sometimes, bird-watching." His implacable expression made her fear she was overacting.

"A cuckoo?" he queried, frowning. "If you did hear one, it's most unusual so early in the season." Suspicion rekindled in the steely eyes.

Oops, thought Nicola in dismay. Bad blunder there. Should have done my research more thoroughly. She'd studied the field guide on the plane coming over and had been up all the previous night with it, but obviously that wasn't enough to make her an expert. However, since she had no alternative but to keep up the pretence, she followed through ingenuously with, "Exactly what I thought! That's why I was so keen to check it out." She was pleased at how convincing she sounded.

He pulled thoughtfully at his beard. "I'm afraid you were probably mistaken, Miss—er..."

"Sharman," she answered. "Nicola Sharman."

"Australian?"

"How *did* you guess?"

He laughed, but she wasn't fooling herself that he was completely disarmed. Those eyes were still ruthlessly assessing her.

Nervously, she asked, "Are you a gamekeeper?"

His dark eyebrows rose as though he were surprised at her question, and again there was a faint, amused smile at the corners of his mouth before he said, "That's one way of describing what I do, I suppose."

A word Nicola had heard somewhere slid into her mind. "I know, you're a *gillie*?" she said. "That's Scottish for rouseabout, isn't it?" Her smile faltered a little at his expressionless look.

He didn't seem as impressed by her knowledge as she'd hoped. "Not exactly." He looked down. "How's the foot now?" He was obviously anxious to send her on her way.

But Nicola was not anxious to go. She put some weight on her foot without actually getting up off the log and grimaced. "All right," she said, wincing to give added realism as she bent over to massage her ankle.

"See if you can stand," he ordered, offering a helping hand.

Nicola gripped it and gingerly stood up. "Ouch!" She gave a deliberately strangled gasp as her foot touched the ground. Hoping he would think she was valiantly trying not to make a fuss, she turned a face full of pain up to his, lips parted slightly in pretended anguish as she bravely took a step. Then, with a flourish that would have done credit to a professional actress, she uttered a sharp cry, stumbled and prepared to crumple at his feet. But he was too quick, and she found herself caught firmly in strong arms and crushed against an unyielding chest in an embrace that made her heart race unexpectedly and her concentration waver.

He spoke first. "Maybe you've sprained your ankle." His voice rumbled down through his chest and into her ear, and she could hear his heart beating a measured rhythm. She surprised herself by thinking how nice and comforting it was to be held like this. Hugh, the only man lately who had held her in his arms at all, was given to swift, passionate embraces, which made her more edgy than relaxed. Was she mad? This man wasn't embracing her. He was furious with her!

"Ye-es, I think I must have," she murmured and then, casting caution to the winds, she played what she hoped would be a trump card. "I-I'm so sorry, but I think I'm going to faint...." She let her whole body slacken and closed her eyes, praying he'd be fooled.

"Oh, for God's sake!" she heard him exclaim under his breath as he supported her.

Nicola held her breath waiting for his next move. When it came it was a shock. He scooped her up bodily and tipped her not altogether gently over his shoulder in a fireman's lift, his arm crooked firmly behind her knees.

"Keep your head down," he advised. Either he assumed she hadn't completely passed out or he was aware she was faking.

He picked up his rifle and slung it over his other shoulder, calling, "Here, Rolf, fetch it, boy!"

Nicola caught a glimpse of the dog picking up her woollen hat in his great jaws. As the gamekeeper strode towards the house with his burden, the dog followed, giving Nicola an occasional look from large, brown, lugubrious eyes.

Nicola hung limply over the broad masculine shoulder, trying not to laugh. Her nerves were tingling now with the thrill of success. This wasn't what she had planned, but it could be working out far, far better than her original scheme. If she could contrive to remain in the house long enough to meet Magnus Lord—and surely he would be curious about an Australian bird-watcher caught trespassing on his land—she might get her interview. She crossed her fingers.

She caught glimpses of the house as the man carrying her crossed the forecourt and marched down a side path. It was a large eighteenth-century stone mansion with high gables and a grey slate roof sprouting chimneys. The mullioned windows were tall and narrow, the walls partially covered in ivy. It looked sombre and forbidding.

Lifting her head a little, Nicola noticed that the blue sky
had vanished under a pall of low cloud and there was a
fine mist drifting across the hills behind the house, ob-
scuring the higher slopes. Switching her gaze to the other
direction, she glimpsed a stretch of grey water that looked
as if it were frozen. On the other side of the loch, sun-
light still illuminated the higher crags and there were
patches of blue sky.

All at once her view was abruptly cut off. She was being carried through a doorway, along a short passageway and into a kind of lobby. At the same moment, her
rescuer or captor, she couldn't quite decide which, called
out loudly, "Binnie!"

He rested his gun against the wall, then deftly rear-
ranged Nicola so that she was clasped against his chest
with her head resting on his shoulder.

A door opened and a grey-haired woman peered at
them over steel-framed spectacles.

"Mercy me!" she exclaimed. "Has there been an accident?"

"No need to panic, Binnie, it's nothing serious," the
bearded man reassured her. "This is Miss Sharman. She
strayed onto the estate to bird-watch and she seems to
have twisted her ankle." His tone was level, his expression unrevealing, giving Nicola no clue as to whether he
believed her genuine or not. Nicola also noticed that he
didn't explain how Rolf had captured her. The man went
on, "I'll put her on the couch in the sitting room. She's
feeling faint. We may have to call Doctor McBride."

Nicola flinched and hoped he wouldn't notice her
sudden stiffening. Wasting a doctor's time wouldn't en-
dear her to anyone.

"Ach, the poor wee lassie!" exclaimed Binnie sym-
pathetically, while Nicola caught a dry glance from the
man in whose arms she was still imprisoned. "I'll bring
ye some sal volatile."

"No, please, I'm all right now," protested Nicola.

Binnie looked doubtful, but she didn't insist. "I expect you'd like a nice cup of tea, though. I'll be away to put the kettle on."

Carrying Nicola through an already open door into a small sitting room, the gamekeeper or *gillie* or whatever he was laid her on a chintz-covered couch. "Binnie Ross is the housekeeper here," he told her.

"Thank you," Nicola muttered, wilting under his gaze. "I'm sorry to be such a nuisance. Er, where exactly am I?"

"At Craigmoor House. On Lord Kilgarrin's estate."

"Oh!" Nicola attempted to look suitably impressed. "I—I hope you'll apologise to him for me. I didn't mean to trespass."

His smile had a sardonic twist. "There's no need to worry. I doubt if he'll want to prosecute you." He added, "I've no doubt he'll be interested to hear about the cuckoo." He gave her a considering look. "Who recommended that you come here to bird-watch?"

Nicola had a rehearsed answer for that question, fortunately. "No one," she replied casually. "I was just driving where the fancy took me. Remote places are where you often make unusual sightings. I thought the moor looked promising."

His gaze was steady, unrevealing. "Perhaps it will prove to have been. Perhaps you did hear a cuckoo, early though it is." A faint smile prefaced his next remark. "What a pity you didn't see it, though. A sighting is always the best confirmation."

"I was interrupted," she reminded him meaningfully and followed the remark with a bright smile.

He looked anything but apologetic and regarded her silently, until Nicola said, "Please don't let me keep you from whatever you were doing, Mr.—er..."

Her question hung in the air for a moment before he answered, reluctantly it seemed to Nicola, "Macpherson. My name's Angus Macpherson."

There was a rattle of crockery on a tray and Binnie stood in the doorway looking, Nicola thought, rather startled by the vehement tone he'd used.

Mrs. Ross recovered herself, came in and put the tray on a table near the couch. "I'll just pour you a cup of tea," she said, "and then I'll see to your poor foot. Milk and sugar?"

"Just black, thanks."

"I brought a cup for you," Binnie said, looking up at Angus. "I thought you might be wanting a drop, too." Without waiting for his answer she bustled out hurriedly as though she'd left something boiling on a stove.

Angus held out his hand. "If you give me your keys, Miss Sharman, I'll bring your car up to the house. If you can't drive it yourself, I'll take you back to the *clachan* later."

"Clachan?" echoed Nicola.

"Craigie Moor. The village. Known hereabouts as a *clachan*—literally a meeting place," he explained. "You're staying at the hotel, presumably?"

"Yes, I was," Nicola said, "but I checked out this morning."

"I see. And where do you plan to spend tonight?"

"I don't know yet," Nicola confessed. "Wherever I end up, I suppose." Suddenly she remembered the old woman's remark and added, "Somewhere safe and sound, I hope." She read in his expression the profound wish that so far as he was concerned, the sooner she found that place, the better.

He flexed his fingers. "The car keys?"

"I left them in the ignition," Nicola told him.

He regarded her for a moment, then said, "Your tea's getting cold, Miss Sharman."

"Shall I pour one for you, Mr. Macpherson?" Nicola asked.

"No, thank you," he said, and abruptly left.

CHAPTER TWO

THE room seemed curiously empty after he'd gone. Angus Macpherson was a big man with a forceful personality, the kind of man who would dominate wherever he happened to be. The kind of man who would zealously guard his own privacy and that of anyone who employed him to do so.

Nicola lifted the rose-patterned teacup with an unsteady hand and looked around her. She could scarcely believe her luck. Here she was in Magnus Lord's house, just as she'd hoped to be. It wasn't impossible that at any moment he might come in and accidentally find her. Or when Angus Macpherson told him about her, as surely he would, he might just be curious enough to come and talk to her.

"Please let him come," she whispered nervously. Supposing he did come, would she be able to keep her cool? She must. She would never have an opportunity like this again. Hugh would demote her to secretary or worse if she muffed it.

She let her gaze roam idly around the small, comfortably furnished sitting room, taking in details that would add colour to her story—if she got one. A low fire burned in the grate, and the solid stone mantel was surmounted by a large oil painting of a stag poised on a craggy hillside. The label on it said Lord of the Glen. Maybe Magnus Lord did have a sense of humour. Maybe he wasn't as unreachable as she'd believed, or as his *gillie* appeared to be. She fervently hoped so.

A murmur of voices from outside the room broke into her thoughts. Angus Macpherson's deep rumble was unmistakable, and it seemed there was something amiss, judging by the housekeeper's anxious tone. Nicola, unused to the Scottish accents, caught very little of their rapid exchange until Angus raised his voice impatiently.

"Of course I can manage," Angus said firmly. "Don't be silly, Binnie. You're going, and that's final."

Nicola heard a door slam, and a moment later the door to the sitting room opened, to admit Mrs. Ross with a bowl of water and towels. She looked agitated despite the sympathetic smile she gave Nicola. The housekeeper set the bowl on the carpet beside the couch. "Now, let me see your poor foot," she said in a kindly tone.

Nicola slipped off her boot apprehensively, half expecting Mrs. Ross to tumble at once to what a fraud she was. She almost wished she *had* sprained her ankle.

"It hurt quite badly at first," she muttered, "but that's passed off now. It must have been just an awkward wrench and the pain made me feel faint for a minute or two. There was really no need for Mr. Macpherson to..." She trailed off as Binnie regarded her somewhat curiously over her spectacles.

"I daresay he felt responsible because Rolf frightened you."

So Angus had told her about that, Nicola reflected. At least he was honest.

Binnie wrung out a towel in the bowl and applied it to Nicola's ankle. Nicola flinched. It was icy cold. "There's no swelling," Binnie observed, "but just in case, a few cold compresses won't do any harm." She chuckled. "Rolf's really a gentle dog. He wouldn't hurt a fly, unless ordered to."

"I didn't know that at the time," Nicola pointed out rather drily.

"Lord Kilgarrin used to have a lot of trouble with trespassers," Binnie explained, wringing out the cold towel again.

"Bird-watchers?"

"Aye, a few were interested in birds. But the local clubs, which are the only ones he allows, always make arrangements in advance if they want to come." She didn't confide the nature of the other trespassers, but Nicola didn't need to ask.

After a pause, Nicola ventured, "From what Mr. Macpherson said, I gathered Lord Kilgarrin is very interested in birds himself."

"Aye. It's a pity he's away at the moment. He'd have been verra interested to know that you heard a cuckoo." She glanced up and smiled at Nicola, who was trying valiantly not to show her intense disappointment at discovering that her quarry was not at home.

It was a possibility she hadn't ignored, of course, but it complicated her plan. She mentally crossed her fingers, hoping that he wouldn't be absent long and that she could somehow persuade Mr. Macpherson to let her birdwatch on the estate for a few days. She had brought a tent and a sleeping bag, but maybe she wouldn't have to use them. Binnie was the sort of kindly soul who would almost certainly offer her hospitality, Nicola thought. And this big old house must have plenty of spare rooms. The big question was, would Mr. Macpherson be persuadable?

The housekeeper was saying reassuringly, "I don't think there's much wrong with your ankle, my dear, but I'll put a bandage round it for support." To Nicola's relief, she added, "I don't think you need the doctor."

When the housekeeper had finished, Nicola felt her bandaged ankle gingerly. "It feels fine. Thank you very much, Mrs. Ross. I'm sorry to have been such a nuisance, and it's kind of you to go to so much trouble."

"Not at all." Light hazel eyes twinkled behind the spectacles. "We canna have ye going back to Australia telling your friends and family that the Scots are inhospitable folk, now can we?"

Nicola saw that she had been mistaken in thinking that all Scots were dour. Like his *gillie*, Magnus Lord's housekeeper had a talent for sly mockery.

Nicola laughed. "It'll make a good story, though."

"Story?" The question was sharp, the eyes instantly suspicious. The press might have left Magnus Lord alone for years, but his staff were evidently still on the alert.

"To dine out on," said Nicola hastily. "My bird-watching friends will have a good laugh at my expense. My reputation at my club will be in tatters."

Mrs. Ross studied her thoughtfully, but didn't ask any questions. She still seemed a little distracted, Nicola thought, as though something were on her mind—whatever it was she and Angus Macpherson had been arguing about, presumably.

"What exactly does a *gillie* do, Mrs. Ross?" Nicola enquired casually. "Besides gamekeeping."

Binnie showed surprise at the question. "Now, why would you want to know that?"

"Oh, I just read the word somewhere. I presumed it's what Mr. Macpherson is, rather like what we would call a rouseabout or a labourer, isn't it?"

Unexpectedly, Binnie's lips pursed and she said rather stiffly, "Mr. Macpherson is not a *gillie*, nor a gamekeeper. He's the estate manager."

Nicola heard this with deep dismay. What a gaffe she'd made. She bit her lip. "Oh, dear," she murmured. It was unlikely he would do her any favours if he thought she'd insulted him. Nicola cursed herself for jumping to conclusions.

"I'll get ye a drop o' fresh hot water for that tea. Ye'll be fancying another cup, I'm thinking," said Binnie, and before Nicola could beg her not to bother, she had gone again.

Now, what would Hugh do in my shoes? Nicola thought desperately. He'd think of something—maybe an excuse for coming back when Magnus Lord was at home? She racked her brains. "Got it!" she exclaimed finally. She would contrive to leave something behind, her watch perhaps, by shoving it down the side of the couch. Though for that to work, she must find out when Magnus Lord was expected home, without giving away why she wanted to know.

The housekeeper returned briefly, bringing a silver pot of hot water and a dish of oatcakes. "Just out of the oven," she announced. "Try some if ye'd care to, and then have a wee rest. Prop your foot up for a while and it'll not give you much trouble, I'm sure." She disappeared again before Nicola even had a chance to strike up a conversation.

After Mrs. Ross had gone, she poured herself another cup of tea and glumly faced the possibility that she might well have to admit defeat, after all. She watched the flames in the fireplace dancing and listened for the sound of her car being driven up to the house, but she heard nothing. And Angus Macpherson didn't come near her again. She placed her empty cup and saucer back on the tray and sighed. A moment later she was fast asleep.

She awoke with a start to find that she was no longer alone. Angus Macpherson was standing over her. He looked like a powerful clansman with a captive, she thought, assembling colourful images automatically. He had changed his outdoor clothes for dark brown trousers—Nicola would have preferred a kilt—and a cream Arran sweater. His dark, wavy hair swept back boldly from a broad high forehead and curled up along the neckline of his sweater. His blue-grey eyes had a piercing quality and his strong, well-defined mouth was accented by a full beard. The beard made it difficult to guess his age. He could be as old as forty, or he could be much younger. Nicola wondered how long he had been watching her and what he was thinking. He certainly looked like a man who was making judgements. Why couldn't he have been away and Magnus Lord at home? Nicola thought resentfully.

"Awake at last." The melodic tones of his soft Highland accent set her nerve ends tingling as Nicola threw off her lethargy and sat up. She glanced at her watch and was amazed to find she had slept, not for a few minutes, but for several hours. The long drive yesterday, her lack of sleep last night, and today's shocks and surprises, had taken an unexpected toll.

She leaped up. "Oh, I'm sorry. The fire was very warm, and I must have dozed off." He was so close that she almost bumped him under the chin as she stood up. His right hand clasped her shoulder and pushed her back onto the couch.

"Don't panic! Remember your ankle."

For a moment she'd forgotten it. She said quickly. "My ankle's all right now. It was only a slight wrench, thank goodness, but it hurt like the devil when I did it. I'd better go." There was no way she was going to try and persuade this formidable man to let her stay. He'd discover the truth in seconds and would probably take great pleasure in throwing her out. She wasn't even prepared to risk trying to find out Magnus Lord's movements from him. He was bound to be suspicious.

Hugh would just have to do without the Magnus Lord story, and she would have to do without rapid promotion, and, well, Hugh probably hadn't been serious about marrying her, anyway. And she certainly didn't want marriage as a reward for good work. Suddenly she saw her feelings for her top boss for what they were—mere infatuation. The nerve of him, patronising her as he had done. Well, she wasn't that much of a fool, and she wasn't in love with Hugh Vanter. She was surprised that she'd ever thought she might be.

"You're not going anywhere tonight."

Nicola stared at him uncomprehendingly. "I beg your pardon?" His appraisal was slow, thorough and a little nerve-racking.

He said emphatically, "The mist has come down early and it's thickening. You'd probably get lost. So I'm afraid you'll have to remain here tonight."

"Mist," Nicola repeated, and there was an uncanny echo in her mind. The old shepherdess had warned her about the mist before nightfall, but that was surely only a weather forecast, not a true prophecy. And yet it had provided just the break she needed. Who knows what might happen tomorrow? she thought, her mood suddenly optimistic again.

Angus said, "Binnie has made up a room for you and I've taken your luggage up. You'll find a bathroom opposite your bedroom."

Not wanting to appear too eager, Nicola got up and crossed to the nearest window. "Are you sure it's too foggy for me to drive?" When she pulled back one of the thick velvet curtains to peer out, she received her answer. All she could see in the gathering gloom was impenetrable greyness. She turned around. "Yes, I see what you mean." She apologised again. "I'm sorry to be putting you to all this trouble."

"No trouble," he assured her. "Come down and have a drink before dinner. In here, when you're ready." A ghost of a smile underlined the hospitable gesture.

Nicola was surprised and gratified by the invitation. She hadn't expected him to be that civil. After all, in his eyes she was a trespasser. He had no obligation to have dinner with her. Perhaps he wasn't so dour, after all, she thought, her optimism increasing. Perhaps fate *was* taking a hand.

His gaze travelled slowly down the length of her. "Your ankle must be much better."

Since she had forgotten again and automatically walked to the window without limping, she had to say, "Yes, I can walk on it quite comfortably now. Mrs. Ross's cold compresses have worked wonders."

"In that case, you may be able to go chasing after cuckoos tomorrow, after all," he said blandly, the polite, cool smile failing to mask the mocking glint in his grey eyes.

He escorted her to the stairs and pointed upwards. "Turn left at the top," he instructed. "Yours is the fourth room along."

He talks as though he owned the place, Nicola thought. But of course a man like Magnus Lord would no doubt leave the running of his estate and even his household to his manager. And a man who acted as a sort of bodyguard, as well, would naturally be familiar with his employer's surroundings. Besides, Angus Macpherson didn't strike her as the kind of man to act in a servile manner.

She sensed that he was watching her as she walked upstairs, and when she glanced back from the landing, he was indeed still standing below, head raised, grey eyes directed at her. Nicola smiled, but as she turned away she had the disquieting feeling that he was laughing at her— probably because she had proved herself singularly inept as a bird-watcher.

She found her room easily. Suitcase, purse and airline bag were there, together with her backpack and binoculars and the woollen hat Rolf had retrieved. Nicola opened her case to find something suitable to wear for dinner. Since she had brought few clothes with her, there was only one possible choice: a deep purple velvet skirt that went well with a black top. The top had a low neck-line and tight-fitting, wrist-length sleeves. With this outfit Nicola usually wore a gold belt and gold necklace for a touch of glamour, but when she put them on she felt overdressed, so she removed the belt.

As she brushed her hair, combing the thick bangs over her forehead almost to the line of her eyebrows, she decided she must apologise to Angus Macpherson for mistaking him for an estate labourer. Perhaps then he would thaw a little.

Sliding her feet into black high-heeled sandals, she sighed. If only fate had been a bit more kind, she could have been having dinner tonight with Magnus Lord instead of with his manager. It occurred to her then that perhaps this was better, after all. If her apology softened Angus, as she hoped it would, she might even decide to confess to him who she really was, she thought daringly. But only if she judged there was a chance that he would agree to persuade Magnus to let her interview him when he returned. If she could make an ally of Angus Macpherson, she would be home free. "Hugh, darling, you would be proud of me," she mocked, with just a twist of bitterness in her smile.

Nicola surveyed herself in the mirror, then buckled on the gold belt, after all, and added a little blusher to her cheeks and mascara to her eyelashes. She grinned at her reflection. Wasn't she being just a little too sure of herself, imagining she could charm a man as intimidating as Angus Macpherson into doing what she wanted? Just because Michael O'Flynn had been a pushover didn't mean anyone else would be. Hugh had manipulated her, she now realised with some chagrin, pushed her into this escapade while she was still flushed with the success of her previous interview. It was her own fault, though, for being flattered enough to let him succeed.

When Nicola returned to the sitting room, she found Angus standing in front of the fire, one elbow resting on the mantel, a glass in his hand. Rolf was lying on the hearth rug, almost completely covering it. The dog's head lifted as Nicola entered, and she hesitated as he fixed his intent brown eyes on her and growled softly.

"It's all right, Rolf," Angus said, and the dog relaxed. Angus then reassured a slightly nervous Nicola. "He knows you're a bona fide visitor now, and he's not allowed to eat guests."

Nicola pinned on a wary smile and approached cautiously nonetheless.

"Is he a Great Dane?" she asked, keeping her distance from the dog.

"Yes. He's a very lovable animal, really. Soft as a cushion in fact. But he's been trained to scare the living daylights out of trespassers."

"Is he yours or Lord Kilgarrin's?"

"Oh, he's Magnus's dog," Angus answered. He seemed to be watching her expression very intently, as if he were weighing her up.

Nicola avoided looking at him. "It's kind of you to have dinner with me, Mr. Macpherson," she said, "but I feel rather guilty about it. Wouldn't you, er, normally go home for dinner?"

"I'm living here at the moment," he answered. "The Rowans, my house on the estate, is being redecorated."

So he wasn't purposely being hospitable towards her, Nicola realised. It was just that he had no alternative but to share a meal with her. He hadn't mentioned a wife or family, she noted, neither his nor Lord Kilgarrin's. So it seemed likely Magnus Lord hadn't married again. She longed to ask some personal questions, but didn't dare to. Not yet, anyway.

"A drink?" he offered.

"Thank you. A dry sherry, if you have it."

The grey eyes were riveting. "Would you like to try a real, aged malt whisky? We don't let much of the genuine stuff out of Scotland, you know. It's much too precious, and there isn't enough of it."

"You can spare some for trespassers?" she queried lightly.

"Pretty ones," he rejoined, the corners of his mouth turning up slightly, and she pulled a face.

"In that case..."

Angus poured a measure of clear golden liquid into a heavy crystal glass and glanced across at her. "I would advise adding a little water until you're used to it."

"Whatever you say." She noticed that he didn't dilute his own generous measure. He handed over her glass, then raised his own, saying with a slow smile, "Here's to the prettiest bird-watcher ever to venture out of the antipodes!"

Nicola returned teasingly, "And to the handsomest *gillie* she's ever likely to meet in the Old Country!" Lowering her lashes, she added, "I'm sorry I called you that. Mrs. Ross explained, but I should have realised. You don't look like a labourer."

"Don't I? Well, that's comforting, I suppose. What do I look like?"

She wanted to say, Like a handsome clan chieftain and probably more like an aristocrat than Lord Kilgarrin himself, but that might have sounded too flattering and made him suspicious. So she said, "Well, I did think you were a gamekeeper at first—that's a bit above a *gillie*, isn't it?"

He laughed. "I don't think we should argue over job descriptions. My ego isn't in the least deflated, I assure you." He caught hold of her free hand and drew her towards the couch. "Let's sit over here. It's too warm by the fire." He kept hold of her hand as they sat, and leaning towards her, urged, "Go on, try it."

Nicola, allowing her fingers to remain imprisoned in his, took a sip from the glass in her other hand, rolled it around her tongue and swallowed. It wasn't as fiery as she had expected. She was pleasantly surprised by the smoothness of it and by its mellow taste. "It's delicious." And as the whisky's inner fire began to warm her blood, she added, "But I bet it's potent."

He just smiled. "Don't forget to buy a bottle to take home with you." Then he added, fixing her with rather a piercing stare, "How long do you plan to stay in Scotland? It is a sight-seeing as well as a bird-watching trip, I presume?"

Nicola decided it must be the whisky more than her apology that was making him so agreeable. "It's my first visit to Scotland, so I want to see everything," she said enthusiastically and, as it happened, truthfully.

"And what do you do when you're not on holiday or bird-watching?" Angus asked abruptly.

Nicola, caught momentarily off her guard, had to improvise rapidly. "I, er, work in an office." That was true enough.

"What kind of office work?" he enquired with polite interest, but with a certain sharpness of tone.

Nicola swallowed hard, but found she wasn't game enough yet to divulge the truth. She must be careful not to reveal herself until she was sure there was a good chance he would agree to her request. To show her hand too soon might ruin everything.

"Public relations," she answered. That was only bending the truth a little, she thought virtuously.

"How very interesting," he murmured. "And bird-watching is your weekend hobby?" Again there was a hint of humour in his eyes and a suggestion of doubt in his voice.

"One of them." She didn't mind his patronising her. They had to make small talk about something. Inspired, she added, "I'm only a beginner, really."

He made no comment, but held out his hand for her empty glass and filled it. "Where do you live and work?" he asked. "Sydney? Melbourne?"

"Sydney."

He handed the glass to her, but remained standing. "Lucky you. It's a fine city. That harbour!"

"You've been there?"

"Once or twice," he acknowledged, but gave Nicola no opportunity to quiz him, instead continuing rapidly with his own inquisition. "I couldn't help noticing the camera sticking out of your backpack, Miss Sharman. You're a keen photographer?"

Under the spell of his voice, while wondering if it was the malt whisky that gave the Highland accent its special quality, Nicola's mind had momentarily wandered again, and now a warning bell sounded as the resonantly rolling *r*s brought her attention back.

"Oh, yes, very keen," she said, stretching a smile. She didn't of course tell him she'd done a crash course in photography before the O'Flynn assignment or that Barry, the chief photographer for *Private Lives,* had said she had what it took to be a good one. He'd been very complimentary about her O'Flynn pictures and had given her a lot of sound advice.

"You're a professional?" Angus murmured, his eyes lingering on her face, then drifting across her bare throat and down to the slight swell of her breasts above the low neckline. Nicola flinched in alarm, but was relieved when he went on, "There's a good market for first-rate wildlife photography. Is that why you've taken up bird-watching?"

Nicola heaved a sigh of relief and confessed modestly, "No, I only take pictures for my own interest." She laughed. "And to bore my friends."

"You carry expensive, sophisticated equipment for an amateur. That camera is a beauty."

Nicola didn't need to be reminded. It was a compliment that Barry had allowed her to borrow it. It might have been a good moment to confess everything, but Nicola was still far from confident that he would react in the way she wanted him to. Those blue-grey eyes regarding her so intently and glinting in the firelight were not only compelling, they were positively intimidating. It was the point at which Hugh would probably have advised plunging in had he been at her elbow, but she wasn't hardened enough by experience to be so reckless.

But her imagination was always bubbling, so she plunged instead into an off-the-cuff invention, hoping it would give her all the more to laugh about later. "My father gave me the camera," she said. Well, Barry was a sort of father figure. "He likes giving expensive presents, and he can afford it. My mother's dead so he has no one else to indulge."

"So you're a spoilt little rich girl?" The grey eyes were faintly derisive.

Nicola immediately regretted the image she'd given him of herself. "I don't think so. I work for a living."

"Yes, in public relations, you said." His tone suggested he didn't have much time for that profession and probably thought it frivolous. "What does your father do? A tycoon of some sort, I suppose?"

Nicola sought to improve the picture without bending the truth too far. "He's in the hotel industry." Since her father ran a small motel near Coff's Harbour, north of Sydney, it was half true. "As a matter of fact, he's been encouraging me to become a professional photographer. He thinks I could learn, but—" she shrugged "—I don't

know," she finished with modestly downcast eyes. I
ought to write fiction, not fact, she thought, and I ought
not to overact!

There was a weighty pause, and then Angus
Macpherson's eyes suddenly challenged her with thinly
veiled menace. In a voice of cold steel he demanded, "Do
you really expect me to believe that load of drivel? Why
not admit the truth, Miss Sharman? You're a fake.
You're a journalist or a Press photographer, aren't you?
You're hell-bent on interviewing Lord Kilgarrin or
Magnus Lord, and all this rubbish about being a bird-
watcher is just a ruse to try and get near him. Well, I can
tell you right now, you won't. So far as the Press and the
rest of the world are concerned, Magnus Lord no longer
exists. He's Lord Kilgarrin now."

His shock tactics almost worked. Nicola came to the
brink of confessing, but the suddenness of his accusation caused words to evade her temporarily and before
she could speak he was continuing, "Who sent you?
What crummy little colonial muckraking rag do you
represent?" His tone was harsh, his disgust plain.
"You're lucky Magnus isn't here," he added threaten-
ingly. "He'd throw you out."

Nicola bristled with outrage in defence of her magazine. *Private Lives* did not muckrake, it published the
truth; and Nicola's articles had always been approved by
her subjects. It riled her to have her professional integrity smeared, but she managed to keep cool enough to
consider her dilemma rationally. Despite his earlier affability, Angus certainly wasn't in the mood now for the
kind of persuasion she had hoped to bring to bear on
him. He already despised her for being, as he thought,
rather frivolous. The truth would make him despise her
even more, and suddenly she couldn't bear that.

Nicola had no choice but to bluff. Taking a deep
breath, she feigned indignation. "How dare you? How

dare you accuse me like that? Just because I trespassed for the most innocent of reasons, and you happen to be paranoid about journalists. I haven't the faintest idea what you're talking about, or what muckraking there might be to do in your or Lord Kilgarrin's life, but I assure you it's of no interest to me!'' She widened her large green eyes guilelessly and saw with satisfaction that he was taken aback by her realistic performance. ''I've never even heard of Magnus Lord, or whatever he likes to call himself.''

The suspicion hadn't quite faded from his eyes yet. ''Either that was a very good performance, or you're genuine.'' His smile was tight and grim.

Nicola contrived to look bewildered. ''Suppose you tell me what this is all about? What's Lord Kilgarrin—or Magnus Lord—got to hide? Why did you go all apoplectic at the thought I might be a journalist?'' She chuckled to show she wasn't really too offended. ''I like that. Me, mistaken for a daring reporter—wait till I tell Dad.'' She stopped abruptly. She must be careful not to overdo it. ''Well, why did you?'' she repeated.

He hesitated for a moment, then said, ''Never mind.''

Nicola felt it might seem odd if she weren't curious. ''Oh, come on, you've whetted my appetite. Don't be such a tease. Was he a film star?''

''No,'' Angus said firmly, adding, ''I don't discuss Magnus's private life.''

''I see. You're his faithful protector as well as his estate manager? You and Rolf make a formidable team, I have to admit. Do you often have to chase journalists away?''

''Rarely, nowadays,'' he admitted.

A possibility suddenly occurred to her. ''Did you know someone was trespassing before you found me? It wasn't just a coincidence that you happened to be passing just then, was it? Did I set off an alarm?''

To her relief, his suspicions seemed to have been allayed, although he hadn't apologised for his outburst, and he actually chuckled. "Yes. When you came through the gate, which must have accidentally been left unlocked, an alarm sounded in the house. It hadn't gone off for so long I was astounded, even though Old Mairi—" He paused, then continued abruptly, "We have another entrance, you see. A back road. The big gates haven't been used for years."

"I see. And so you armed yourself to the teeth and rushed out to repel the invaders."

"The gun wasn't loaded. It's only for effect. I never actually shoot anyone—or anything." He laughed. "The last thing I expected was an antipodean bird-watcher." The unexpectedness of it still seemed to amuse him.

"That makes me sound like a prehistoric species. Anyway, bird-watching isn't funny, it's fascinating." Nicola spoke with what she hoped was the right degree of indignation, while still showing she had a sense of humour and forgave him for his earlier injustice.

He answered gravely, "Magnus and I would wholeheartedly agree with you."

He wasn't mocking her now. He was tempted to believe her, Nicola thought triumphantly. She was glad, however, when the subsequent silence was abruptly interrupted by Mrs. Ross appearing to tell them dinner was ready. As she walked to the door, Rolf pushed past her and almost caused her to stumble. Angus's hand steadied her.

"Is that the whisky or your ankle?" He was teasing again and the tension had relaxed.

Nicola responded briskly, "It was Rolf. You should teach him that it's ladies first in polite company."

Angus chuckled. "Hasn't the feminist movement reached the colonies yet?"

Nicola refused to be needled. She responded cheerfully to his teasing. "It's been and gone, and by the way, we're not colonies any longer. Don't they teach history in Scotland?"

"No, we'd rather make it," he shot back at her, with a look that was more humorous than arrogant.

Nicola's barely stifled snort of disgust only seemed to amuse him. As he withdrew his hand from her arm, still chuckling, Nicola was suddenly aware of his warm, spicy smell, and a startlingly pleasurable sensation ran through her from the point where his fingers had grasped her.

In the dining room, Angus pulled out a chair for Nicola and pushed it in as she sat. She had the feeling that even if his arch-enemy were to come to dinner, Angus Macpherson would be the soul of politeness.

There was a bottle of wine on the table and Angus proceeded to uncork it. "Binnie said a claret would best complement tonight's meal," he observed.

Nicola was considering whether she ought to risk drinking any more, but she allowed him to fill her glass. "I'm sure Mrs. Ross knows best," she murmured, adding, "Isn't she going to join us?" She had noticed that only two places were set.

Angus said, "Binnie prefers to eat in the privacy of her own flat where she can put her feet up in front of the television. And tonight she'll be anxious to get on with her packing. She's leaving tomorrow for a short holiday. She and her sister in Glasgow are taking a cruise. A month sailing around the Caribbean. Quite daring for two elderly ladies, wouldn't you say?"

"Good for them!" Nicola exclaimed. "Lord Kilgarrin might be upset, though, if his housekeeper meets a millionaire and doesn't come back."

Angus laughed. "I don't think there's much fear of that. Binnie is contemptuous of wealth and very devoted to Magnus. She's positively wretched because the woman

who's supposed to be coming to help out while she's away
has gone down with flu, and with most people off on
their holidays before the summer tourist season begins,
she can't find a replacement. She was all for cancelling
the cruise, but naturally I wouldn't hear of it. Magnus
and I can manage quite well on our own.''

"He won't be away long, then?" Nicola dared to ask.

Angus shrugged. "I don't know. As long as he needs
to be, I suppose. He'll be back when his business is com-
pleted."

And with that, Nicola had to be content, although the
vagueness of the answer was a disappointment.

"Mrs. Ross housekeeps for you, too?" Nicola asked.

He nodded. "She's a rare treasure these days. She's
been with the Kilgarrin family since she was a girl."

Binnie Ross brought in the first course and even while
he chatted to the housekeeper, Nicola was conscious that
Angus's eyes were on her, not Binnie. They were roam-
ing idly across her face, down the slender curve of her
neck and lingering on the pendant at her throat.

Nicola lowered her gaze, finding his too penetrating
and afraid he might read too much in her face. For a
while she concentrated on the meal, but the silence was
uncomfortable and she was glad when Angus broke it.

"You're miles away again."

"Sorry."

"I dare say I'm rather boring company," he commented in a dry tone. "I've never been much good at
small talk and we have few visitors here for me to practise on."

They managed, however, to find enough topics to occupy the remainder of the meal, but Nicola was again
beginning to feel the strain of masquerading by the time
they returned to the sitting room for coffee. Angus stoked
the fire, and it crackled and flared into fresh life, radi-

ating warmth into the room. Nicola sat on the couch, stretched out her legs, feet together, and compared them.

"My ankle doesn't hurt at all now," she remarked. "And I'm sure it's not at all swollen."

Angus bent and clasped his fingers around the bandaged ankle, supporting her calf with the palm of his other hand as he examined it. Nicola flinched at his touch, but not from pain. His smooth, slightly detached yet intimate manner was getting to her in a way she hadn't experienced before with a masculine companion, and she felt uneasy. He displayed all the suave sophistication of a man of the world, but he also behaved with the impeccable manners of a gentleman; and he intrigued her greatly.

Angus rose and walked to the sideboard. "A liqueur, Miss Sharman?"

"No, thank you, Mr. Macpherson."

He persisted. "Can't I tempt you to have a small Drambuie, the favourite liqueur of Bonnie Prince Charlie? It goes down very well with coffee."

"All right," Nicola said recklessly. "Just a very small one."

He poured himself a whisky, bringing it and her glass to the couch while Nicola poured the coffee. Her fingers brushed his as she handed a cup to him and in turn took the glass of Drambuie. Something in the way he looked at her made her avert her eyes hastily. She sipped her liqueur, alternating it with coffee, and for a few minutes they talked idly on innocuous subjects, where she intended to go next and what Angus considered the best places to see. Nicola, warmed by the food and wine, had to force herself to concentrate on not giving herself away. Eventually she couldn't hold back a yawn.

Angus said, "I'm sorry. I'm keeping you up." He looked at her thoughtfully for a moment. "The barometer was rising when I looked at it earlier. It will be a fine day tomorrow, perfect for bird-watching, that is, if you still want to check out that cuckoo."

"I have your permission?"

"Yes, of course."

His offer must mean that her bluff had worked, and Nicola's spirits soared. She hadn't even had to persuade him in the end. If he was amenable to her staying a day, surely he wouldn't object if she wanted to extend it a little? But she'd still have to be careful how she broached it.

They stood up together. "Good night, Mr. Macpherson," Nicola murmured, "and thank you again for your hospitality. I appreciate it very much and I'm sorry to have inconvenienced you."

Angus studied her face in an unhurried way, startled by the thoughts burgeoning in his mind. His mouth tilted in amusement at her guileless expression, the innocence in her extraordinarily vivid green eyes. He was not entirely convinced that she was all she said she was, but she was certainly a woman to set a man's pulse racing as his hadn't done for a long time. Supposing there was more to what Old Mairi had said. She had the gift of the sight, after all, and he had reason not to scoff at that.

"Good night, Miss Sharman," he said at last. "Sleep well."

But Nicola didn't. It was difficult to empty her mind of thoughts of Angus Macpherson. He invaded her dreams vividly, and it was a romantically kilted version of the tall, dark, bearded Scot who enticed her away from an interview with Magnus Lord, swept her masterfully into his arms and onto a coal-black horse, which he rode like the devil across the heather-clad hills in the manner of really old romantic movies.

CHAPTER THREE

IT WAS still dark in her room when Nicola was awakened by the sound of deep-throated barking. She crept across to the window and drew back the curtains. Dawn was just breaking.

Through the dense grey mist that swathed the world she could see little more than the shadowy shapes of outbuildings and the skeletal trees that sheltered the house. She could feel the cold through the glass and shivered, rubbing her bare arms as she retreated into the cosy, centrally heated room. It was too early to get up, so she snuggled back under the covers and let her mind drift over the unexpected twists and turns her plans had taken the previous day.

Her thoughts were presently interrupted by a tap at the door. Mrs. Ross called out, "Are you awake, Miss Sharman?"

"Yes, I am. Come in."

Bearing a tray that emitted steam and delicious aromas, the housekeeper bustled in. "Good morning, my dear. I hope you were comfortable and warm enough." Binnie Ross smiled approvingly as she regarded Nicola over the top of her steel-rimmed spectacles. This girl was definitely not a tough journalist. She sighed. And what if she were? It was time the bitterness ended, anyway.

"Thank you," said Nicola. "I was very comfortable, and beautifully warm. I'm sorry for putting you to all this trouble." As she sat up, the housekeeper placed the breakfast tray on her knees.

"It's no trouble." Mrs. Ross's manner was warm and friendly, but the hazel eyes were curious.

"Is it still foggy?" Nicola asked. "It was when I looked a while ago."

Binnie nodded. "Yes, but it'll have lifted by nine o'clock. Mark my words, it'll be a beautiful day."

Presently, after porridge, scrambled eggs, oatcakes, and toast with homemade blackberry jam, all washed down with strong, fragrant coffee, Nicola got up. As soon as she had bathed and dressed, she carried the breakfast tray downstairs to the kitchen. Her hand was on the doorknob when the sound of Binnie's and Angus's voices checked her briefly because they seemed to be arguing again.

"Ach, I wish I didna have to go," Binnie was saying regretfully. "Why did Morag have to catch the flu now? If I could only think of someone else."

"Stop worrying, Binnie," Angus said. "Everything will be perfectly all right. It'll only be for a few days. But if it'll set your mind at rest, I could ask Rowena if she can oblige."

Nicola's arm was aching from supporting the tray against her hip and suddenly it slipped, rattling the crockery and cutting off the rest of the conversation. She opened the door and went in. As a result of what she had overheard, a brilliant idea was forming in her mind. If she'd been as alert as Hugh expected her to be, it would have occurred to her yesterday, she knew, but at least she hadn't missed her cue altogether. Perhaps now was a more auspicious time to act anyway.

Angus looked up as she came in. His gaze was steady but unreadable, and it sent the wrong kind of shivers racing along her nerves. Nicola tried in vain to stop the colour from flooding her cheeks and wondered if what she proposed to do was such a good idea, after all. Was she that desperate to get her story? Her newly discovered contempt for Hugh said she wasn't, but nevertheless her professional pride wouldn't let her abandon the assignment yet.

"Ach, ye shouldna've bothered," said Mrs. Ross, taking the tray from Nicola's slightly unsteady hands. "But thank ye all the same."

Angus put in crisply, "Good morning, Miss Sharman." His expression gave nothing away, but his formal tone measured the distance he was putting between them.

Nicola replied, "Good morning, Mr. Macpherson."

Angus folded his hands behind his head and tilted his chair back, grey-blue eyes intently regarding Nicola. His gaze moved slowly over her close-fitting jeans and red polo-neck sweater. She had tied her hair back with a red ribbon and her face, with barely a trace of makeup, had a more than usually youthful glow.

The corner of his mouth tilted slightly and she found herself watching his lips with fascination as he went on: "Well, are you fit enough to go bird-watching? You might be lucky and actually spot your cuckoo if you keep your eyes peeled." There was only a hint of mockery in the grey eyes.

Nicola tried not to sound too eager. "Maybe, but I really think I'd better be moving on," she said. "I've caused you more than enough inconvenience." She gave a rueful smile. "I'm sure you're right and it's much too early for cuckoos. I was undoubtedly mistaken."

Angus shrugged. "There are plenty of other interesting birds to see around here, and if your ankle really is better we might even stroll up the mountain." There was a slight pause and then he offered what would have been an irresistible temptation to a genuine bird-watcher. "I could show you some golden eagles."

Nicola tensed. *He* could! Did that mean he was prepared to take her bird-watching himself? Had she convinced him with her story last night? Perhaps this was his way of apologising to her.

Mrs. Ross glanced up from measuring flour into a large mixing bowl. "Don't forget to take the lunch." She pushed a backpack across the table.

Nicola was astounded. He'd apparently taken it for granted that she wouldn't refuse his offer.

Angus said, "Thanks, Binnie. We'll be away just as soon as Miss Sharman has fetched her jacket and binoculars." He turned to Nicola. "Wear your hat. There'll be a cool wind on the high crags, if we get that far."

"Crags," echoed Nicola faintly. She had no head for heights.

"That's where the eagles are." His tone was challenging.

Nicola swallowed. Angus was evidently determined to offer the kind of hospitality he believed a bona fide amateur bird-watcher would appreciate.

"It's very kind of you," she said. "But I don't want to keep you from your work."

He made a dismissive gesture. "Run along. The sooner we set off, the less time will be wasted." He was a man used to giving orders and having them obeyed, Nicola thought as she hurried upstairs.

When Nicola came down again, Binnie was pottering about alone in the kitchen, which was exactly what Nicola had hoped for. If only the housekeeper wasn't going away, she thought. She might have proved a more amenable ally than Angus—although, from what he had said, Mrs. Ross was devoted to her laird, and would therefore be very protective.

"You must be looking forward to your cruise very much," Nicola commented idly, hoping to lead up to making her proposal before Angus returned. "It'll be a wonderful holiday."

"Aye, it will," agreed the housekeeper.

"Mr. Macpherson and Lord Kilgarrin will miss you. The woman who was supposed to come and help out has the flu, I gather."

"I didna want to go," confided Mrs. Ross, "but it's all right now. Angus is going to ask Rowena—she's, er, a friend of his—to come and lend a hand. I don't like him bothering her, but he insisted."

Nicola almost gasped in her disappointment and chagrin. But she had to turn on a smile because at that moment Angus came in. He was wearing a sheepskin-lined jacket zipped up over his sweater, and round his neck hung binoculars that were more powerful than Nicola's. He propped two stout walking sticks against the kitchen table and then handed the one with a top carved from a sheep's horn to Nicola. His own was thicker and more knobbly.

"That one's about your size," he commented. "It'll make climbing easier." He glanced at her left foot. "Are you sure your ankle will stand up to a long walk?"

"It's perfectly okay," she said. "I've taken the bandage off. Obviously I didn't do any real damage."

Binnie said to Angus, "Now you take care. Don't make the lassie walk too far." She frowned as though she didn't altogether approve of the excursion.

"Don't worry, we'll be back in good time to take you to your train," Angus said.

"What about Rowena?" Binnie asked anxiously. "Have you asked her yet?"

"Her number was engaged. I'll call her later. Don't worry, Binnie."

Binnie saw them out the door, remarking, "I guarantee there'll not be a wisp o' mist left by the time you reach The Rowans."

Rolf was waiting eagerly for them. He bounded up, tongue lolling joyfully at the prospect of a long hike. He bumped his nose against Nicola, making her jump back nervously. Angus laughed.

"No need to panic. That only means he's accepted you. He'll guard you with his life now."

Nicola tentatively stretched out her hand and the huge dog allowed her to pat his head. "Good boy, Rolf," she murmured.

They set off across the yard and passed behind the barn onto a path leading to the loch. The mist was indeed rising rapidly and soon the sun began to break through. Alders and willows along the loch's edge formed an eye-catching pattern against the sky and Nicola paused to take a few photographs of the scene. Angus offered a word or two of advice about the light, but otherwise made no comment.

The path took them along the edge of the loch for some distance and then veered towards the hills. Angus didn't speak except to call Nicola to a halt so she could observe some bird or other they had disturbed. He seemed to have dropped his sceptical attitude and was treating her as a serious bird observer. So she must have convinced him, after all, Nicola thought with relief and fresh optimism. She'd get a story out of this, one way or another, she vowed. But for her own satisfaction, not just to please Hugh.

As she was studying what Angus had told her was a chaffinch, Nicola picked up an old stone house half hidden in the trees.

"Is that where you live?" she asked.

"That's The Rowans," Angus confirmed.

After they had passed the house, the track meandered with the aimlessness of the sheep that had made it, deep into the hills.

"Now we're entering Glen Craigie," Angus told Nicola as they walked along the narrow path, Rolf lumbering ahead, his nose to the ground. Then the mountains closed in around them.

They followed the sheep tracks across the foothills and along a deep ravine with a rushing stream that cascaded noisily over rocky falls. Soon they were climbing out of the glen, higher and higher beyond the tree belt and onto the rocky barrenness of the mountain where there was little vegetation apart from tufts of grass, bracken and heather. Angus stopped occasionally to direct Nicola's attention to birds, which were fewer now, or to early-spring wildflowers. Here and there, they saw a few black-faced sheep who fled at their approach, the newly born lambs bleating shrilly as they scampered after their mothers.

There was one thrilling moment for Nicola when Angus halted, lifted his hand to check Nicola, too, then laid a finger against his lips. A magnificent stag stood poised on a rocky outcrop just ahead of them, antlers proudly lifted, eyes wary and nose testing the air. For a moment it stared directly at them, then fled.

"The Lord of the Glen!" Nicola exclaimed.

Angus glanced at her and chuckled. "Come on," he said, marching ahead.

Nicola trudged along behind and was glad of the stout stick Angus had given her. Even so she was soon out of breath and her legs began to ache with the effort of climbing. She didn't look back, afraid it would make her giddy. There were patches of snow on the ground now, lingering in shadowy corners, beneath overhangs and in fissures. Nicola pulled her woollen hat down over her ears because the wind, as Angus had warned, was chilly.

At last he called a halt, looking anxiously at Nicola. "Okay?"

"Just fine," she answered breathlessly, averting her gaze from the precipitous drop to the left of them. It had caught her by surprise and caused a brief wave of nausea.

"Now's the moment to say you've had enough. We can go back if you want to," he offered. "How's the ankle bearing up?"

"It's fine. How much further?"

"Not far, but the next bit is steeper."

There was no way she was going to tell him she had no head for heights. For some reason she didn't want to show any weakness to this man. "I came to see eagles, Mr. Macpherson."

He glanced at her briefly and, half smiling, said, "Angus is the name. And yours is Nicola, I believe." He strode on and Nicola trudged resolutely after him, pleased that he had suggested the familiarity himself.

The going was harder, as he had warned, and once or twice Nicola almost slipped on the shifting stones that littered the track, falling behind a little. Angus waited for her to catch up, and they rested for a few minutes.

Angus pointed into the distance. "That's Craigmoor House over there with the loch behind it."

Nicola forced herself to look while clinging surreptitiously to a rock. Angus swept his arm further round. "And that way is the sea. On a clear day you can just see the Isle of Skye. It's too hazy today."

Nicola, fighting giddiness, glanced upwards at the forbidding crags. "How much further now?"

"A bit higher if you want to see the eagles—and if you can manage it." He clamped a hand on her shoulder and liquid warmth seemed to course through her veins. "There are no prizes for exhausting yourself," he said, "so say if you've had enough. I don't want to have to carry you down."

"I'll walk down, don't worry," Nicola promised, and thought it was bound to be worse going back, so why didn't she give in now? But some stubborn streak in her urged her on. She managed to keep up with him for a good distance, but she was glad when he finally called another halt. "This is as far as we go," he announced. "The eyrie is visible from the other side of that overhang, but it's bound to be very windy there, so we can have lunch on this side."

Nicola subsided thankfully onto a boulder while Angus slipped off the backpack containing their lunch. Having regained her breath, she divested herself of her own pack containing her camera equipment, and placed it carefully on the ground.

"You'll need your camera," Angus reminded her. He bent down. "I'll carry it."

"I can manage, thanks." Nicola hoisted the pack up again over her shoulder.

Their eyes met, too close for comfort. "You'll need to take extra care. I'll carry it," Angus insisted and took it from her. Nicola decided not to argue.

With her binoculars swinging around her neck, she scrambled after him to the other side of the overhang. She took a deep breath and shuddered when she saw where he had brought her—a narrow plateau overlooking a deep ravine. They were probably only a thousand feet up, but to Nicola it felt like the top of Mount Everest.

Above the ground haze, the sky was intensely blue and there were feathers of cloud that seemed almost within reach. Only a vapour trail from a jet reminded her of civilisation. This was nature, raw and beautiful. All at once it gave Nicola a feeling of both humility and strength as well as a strange contentment that made her forget all weariness and, momentarily, her fear of heights.

Angus's hand on her shoulders aroused her. He turned her slightly. "Look this way."

She followed his pointing finger and saw an eagle rising above a crag on the other side of the ravine. She raised her binoculars, focused them, then gasped. What had been little more than a brown dot in the sky was suddenly a dramatic picture. The proud head, the savage eye and beak, the effortless spread of the gigantic wings where tips were splayed out like fingers, made a spectacular sight. The bird circled slowly, heading first towards them, then away, tilting its wings on the turns, spreading its tail, totally at ease in its environment. Nicola was transfixed, and when the golden eagle suddenly closed its wings, pointed its head towards the earth and dived, she was so thrilled she cried out, her excited shriek echoing across the crags.

She glanced at Angus, speechless, and he smiled. His eyes were alight with excitement, too.

"Grand sight, eh?" he asked softly.

"Wonderful," she breathed, exhilarated and temporarily forgetful of the fearful chasm below. All at once she was conscious of a closeness with Angus because of it. It was a shared experience such as she had never really had with anyone before, let alone a stranger—and least of all with a man. It was a feeling of oneness that was almost sensual.

"Let's sit over there for a while," Angus said at last, indicating a more sheltered spot.

As Nicola stabbed her walking stick into the ground, it struck the edge of a stone and slipped, causing her to stumble. Fear rushed back in a nauseating wave as the mountain began to tilt and panic gave her a brief sensation of falling, although she was nowhere near the edge.

"Careful." A strong hand gripped and steadied her, and Angus kept a tight hold on her until they were both sitting next to a boulder. With her back against the massive rock, Nicola was in control again. She hoped Angus hadn't seen her irrational fear.

"The eyrie is on a ledge about halfway down that crag," Angus told her. "Can you spot it?"

It was less disconcerting looking through binoculars. Nicola focused hers, scanning the sheer cliff face on the other side of the ravine until she found what she was seeking.

"Got it!" she exclaimed in triumph. There was an eagle standing on the edge of the rough pile of sticks that formed the nest.

Angus said, "That's the female. Here comes the male now."

As Nicola watched, the male eagle landed on the other side of the nest and carefully folded his wings. "Magnificent," she whispered. "Absolutely magnificent."

"You sound as though you've never seen eagles before."

Nicola flinched. "Of course I have. We have eagles in Australia."

"Wedge-tails. They're related to the European golden eagle."

Nicola almost said "Are they?" but stopped herself in time. It would be more convincing if she appeared to know something about the birds back home, so she hazarded: "Yes, it's amazing, isn't it? I suppose there was a migration at some point."

His gaze made her feel a little uncomfortable, it was so penetrating. "Tell me, do farmers still shoot wedge-tails down under, or are they a protected species?"

Nicola was sure he knew the answer, but would expect even a rank amateur to know it, too. She thought it safest to say, "They're protected, of course."

Evidently she had passed the test, if a test it had been, for he didn't quiz her any more, but said, "Fortunately, the eyrie is inaccessible to anyone who isn't an expert rock climber. That pair have raised at least one chick every year for several years now. Golden eagles were practically shot out of the Highlands a while back, but the population is gradually picking up again."

"Why were they shot?" asked Nicola, enthralled by the haughtily regal expression on the birds' faces and forgetting she really ought to know.

A slightly cool look came her way again, as he answered, "Gamekeepers believed they decimated the pheasants and grouse. Farmers blamed them for loss of lambs. But in reality, they take more rabbits than anything else, which is really a service. I trust Australian farmers have learned that lesson, too."

Nicola lowered her binoculars. "How could anyone kill such magnificent creatures? They've got to eat to live, haven't they? And surely they've a right to live. We ought to be able to share with them." She spoke with a depth of feeling she hadn't realised she possessed and gave a faintly embarrassed smile.

Angus said nothing, but his gaze trapped hers and Nicola again had the strangest feeling that for the moment at least, there was complete rapport between them. For her it was even more than that. Being with him had stirred feelings in her she hadn't known existed. Suddenly she hated deceiving him and longed to tell him the truth, to throw herself on his mercy; but the knowledge that if she did she might destroy the moment and tarnish the experience, stopped her from taking the risk. She might never see this man again after today, but she wanted to treasure a perfect memory of it and she didn't want him to despise her. It was an odd sensation and one she didn't feel entirely at ease with. This wasn't the way she was accustomed to being affected by a man, particularly not one who was a complete stranger and whose attitude towards her had at first been anything but friendly.

Angus regarded her with a curious stillness, yet she felt there were unexpected thoughts going through his mind, too. It was uncanny, and then abruptly the moment passed. Angus said, "Aren't you going to take some pictures?"

In her excitement, Nicola had forgotten about photographs, but now she eagerly removed her camera from the backpack and screwed in the telephoto lens. She took a whole series of shots, changing lenses and filters to give her the best chance of success. Angus offered a few suggestions as to speeds and apertures, which suggested that he was an experienced photographer himself.

"You know what you're talking about," Nicola commented. "Is photography one of your hobbies?"

"When I have time. The estate keeps me pretty busy."

"I appreciate your taking a day off for me." It would have been the ideal moment to suggest repaying him by standing in for Morag, but she had had that brain wave a little too late. He was bound to prefer his friend, Rowena. Of course, if Rowena was unable to come... But she wasn't going to anticipate that possibility by offering herself as an alternative now. Wait and see, she cautioned her impatient self.

"I'm enjoying it." He even sounded as though he meant it. "I hope you are."

"Definitely." She turned her attention back to the birds and, after a moment or two, exclaimed in frustration, "What I really need is a movie camera!" She glanced across at him as she spoke, and was in time to catch a fleeting expression that might have been suspicion again, but all he said was:

"I'm sure Daddy would oblige if you mentioned it."

Nicola decided she had better act offended. "There's no need to be sarcastic. Some people make very good home movies." Daringly she added, "With such wonderful subjects as eagles on your doorstep I'm surprised you and Magnus haven't filmed them yourselves, as you seem to be so keen on birds."

He answered shortly, "We don't have the time."

Nicola moved further away from him again, disturbed by his effect on her. Concentrating on the more comfortable perspectives the camera lens gave her, she moved about confidently, forgetting her fear, and in her enthusiasm didn't notice how close to the edge she was straying until, intent on focusing a shot, elbows pressed tightly against her sides to steady the camera, she was suddenly startled by an exclamation from Angus.

"Watch out, there. Don't go too close to the edge!"

Momentarily startled by the warning, Nicola lowered her camera and foolishly looked down. The ravine yawned below her, so near that a horrifying sensation of being dragged downwards gripped her and she teetered giddily. The next moment she was sprawled on the ground, Angus's body covering hers, his arms encircling her tightly. She heard the sickening sound of the stones they had disturbed rattling over into the abyss.

Angus's beard scraped her cheek. "You little fool, you nearly went over." His face was as white as hers. Then realisation dawned. "My God, Nicola, you're afraid of heights, aren't you?"

She nodded weakly and covered her face with her hands. He dragged her back to the rock wall, well away from the edge.

"You idiot," Angus exploded. "Why didn't you say you suffered from vertigo? I'd never have dreamt of bringing you up here if I'd known. And you—are you mad, cavorting about on the edge of a precipice when you know damn well—?"

"It doesn't bother me when I'm looking through a camera lens or binoculars," she said. "I'm all right, Angus."

He seemed more shaken, if it were possible, than she was herself. He pulled her upright and turned her face against his side, one broad palm laid protectively across her cheek. "Don't look. We'll get away from here. It's not so bad back where we left the lunch."

They stumbled to the other side of the overhang. Angus, still holding her protectively, looked down into her face. "We'll go down right away if you like."

She shook her head. "No. It's beautiful here. I love it. Truly. I won't look down."

"Sure?"

"Positive."

Angus called to Rolf and they returned to where they had left the lunch. The wind was less blustery there and the sun warmed the grassy patch amid the boulders. Nicola removed her woollen hat and let her ponytail swing free. Her cheeks were pink from the bracing air, and she was able to smile now. On the wider plateau she felt normal again.

"I daresay you've never climbed Ayers Rock?" Angus joked, his own tension relaxing.

Nicola thought of the great central Australian monolith and shuddered. "No way! When I did a trip up there, I bought a T-shirt saying I *Didn't* Climb Ayers Rock."

Angus laughed and squeezed her shoulders. "You've got a lot of nerve, nonetheless. Now let's have the food. I'm ravenous."

"Men are always hungry," said Nicola in a long-suffering voice. "All right, I'll unpack if you gather up afterwards."

"I thought you said feminism had come and gone in the antipodes," he reminded her, grinning.

"It left its mark," she rejoined, and feigning offence, added, "I wish you wouldn't keep calling it the antipodes. The place I come from does have a name: Australia."

"I'm sorry," he said with mock contrition. "I've always had a feeling for the word and this is the first time I've had a chance to use it."

"I know what you mean," said Nicola, suddenly serious. "I love those big words that you read but never say, and if you do, you usually pronounce them wrongly. My favourite is *epitome* and you can guess how I pronounce it if I don't think first."

Their shared laughter bounced off the crags and echoed in the still, mountain air. As it died, Nicola handed a packet of sandwiches to Angus, marvelling at how happy she felt, despite the deception she was practising.

They ate their lunch mostly in silence, but it was a companionable one and Nicola knew she was going to cherish this day for a long time, forever perhaps. It was like being in a kind of time warp, doing something that could never be repeated. And that thought unexpectedly made her feel sad. Why were some of life's most wonderful experiences so fleeting? And why did they always happen at the wrong times?

She glanced at Angus now and then, wondering about him. He seemed so aloof and yet there were moments when, although he was a stranger, she felt as close to him as to a good friend. Perhaps you always felt that way about someone who had saved your life, she thought; but knew she'd begun to feel it even before then. It was a pity she would never have the chance to get to know him better. Their paths had crossed, but in totally impossible circumstances.

Her curiosity about him finally persuaded her to ask, "Angus, have you always lived in the Highlands?" She was much more interested in him now, she realised guiltily, than in the shadowy Magnus Lord, who would have none of this man's vibrant personality, she was sure. The flesh-and-blood Angus Macpherson was much more real and intriguing. But Hugh wouldn't thank her for a story about him, she thought with inward laughter.

He glanced sharply at her. "Why do you ask?"

"I just wondered. I wondered if you'd ever had other jobs before you became manager of the Craigmoor estate." He'd given her the impression he had travelled.

He twisted a blade of grass between long, square-tipped fingers. "I moved around a bit when I was young." His tone discouraged further probing.

Nicola didn't want to spoil their companionableness, so she curbed her curiosity. Soon he stood up, saying, "We'd better start back. I promised to drive Binnie to Fort William to catch her train. Mustn't let her miss it."

As they walked down the winding sheep tracks, leaving the high crags to the birds, Rolf sped eagerly on ahead. Angus kept a hand firmly on Nicola's arm and glanced at her from time to time as he enquired, "All right?" The knowledge that once they reached the bottom of the mountain and entered Craigmoor House, she would be back in real time again, made her feel a very poignant regret.

They were almost back at the house when Angus said, "Good girl. You made it." He caught her firmly by the shoulders, resisting the urge to shake her, it seemed, as he admonished severely, "Don't ever take risks like that again just because of foolish pride or whatever it was that made you go up the mountain with me."

"I got some good pictures, I hope," she said. "It was worth it."

He raked his hair. "Not for me it wasn't. Not for the fright you gave me."

"I'm sorry. One has to face fears to overcome them, though." Nicola touched his arm tentatively. "Thank you, Angus. And my apologies if I caused you any anxiety up there. Thanks again for the eagles. It was wonderful." But it hadn't just been the eagles. There had been other magic moments that she hardly dared believe had happened.

She put them out of her mind, remembering what her real purpose in being there was. If she was to interview Magnus Lord, she had to prolong her stay somehow. She didn't want to ask if she could linger, she wanted Angus to invite her. So a few yards further on, Nicola took a chance. "I think I'll try and reach Skye tonight. The ferries run until quite late, don't they?"

Angus, directing a warm smile at her, answered exactly the way she wanted him to. "There's no need for you to rush off tonight. You're too tired, for one thing." He paused, looked steadily at her for a moment as though considering a decision, then offered, "Why not stay around here for a few days? The estate offers excellent bird-watching. I noticed you have a tent in your boot. You could go off camping if you wished. There are some lovely spots along the edge of the loch, and masses of water birds."

He sounded as though he were actually trying to persuade her. When Angus Macpherson got steamed up, she thought, he really let fly as he had last night, but when he decided to apologise, even if he couldn't bring himself to do it in words, he more than made up for his earlier behaviour in generous gestures.

"That's very kind of you," Nicola murmured, but in a doubtful tone.

"You haven't booked in anywhere," he reminded her. "And you said yourself your schedule was flexible."

It was too good to be true. He was practically giving her *carte blanche* to stay around until Magnus Lord got back, and without her even having to ask. "Well, yes, that's true," she conceded. "And this is a superb spot."

"So you might as well make the most of it."

"All right, I will. If you're sure you don't mind?"

He answered with a look that made her heart flutter like a captive bird's, and when he pulled her into his arms and joined his lips gently to hers, her astonishment was quickly replaced by emotions she knew she had only explored lightly until now.

Angus kissed her with a long, slow sweetness to which she responded with all her natural instincts, and with no fear of the undercurrent of rising passion between them. Briefly she wondered how she could ever have thought kissing Hugh was pleasurable. Hugh took but gave little. Angus gave everything to a kiss. Nicola closed her eyes, amazed at the joyous surge that filled her. She experienced the same exhilaration she'd felt up on the lofty crags with the majestic eagles flying as high as the clouds. It was as though she, too, had the power of flight for a brief, exquisite moment.

Angus suddenly lifted his head, looking startled, either at his own impetuous action or her equally impulsive response. Then he smiled a rather embarrassed smile. "Consider that an apology."

"What for?" she answered huskily.

He tilted her chin, and the grey eyes that looked into hers were teasing. "For doubting you. And for thinking you were spoilt. You aren't."

"I'm not?" Suddenly she felt extremely spoiled indeed.

He tucked her arm through his. "Come on. Binnie will be getting worried about us."

As he'd said, Nicola repeated to herself, it was just an apology, and she mustn't imagine anything else, but when it came to apologising, Angus Macpherson certainly ran rings around anyone else. If she'd wanted proof that she had allayed his suspicions about her completely, the kiss had given it to her. However, she was under no illusions as to how he would react if she told him who she really was. The only person she was going to confess that to, she thought, was Magnus Lord himself. He couldn't be more volatile than Angus, and there was just a chance he would be more forgiving.

When they arrived back at the house there was still plenty of time to spare before Angus had to drive Mrs. Ross to her train. They found the housekeeper in the kitchen, busy making last-minute preparations for dinner. She insisted on fixing them a cup of tea and bringing them a plate of scones.

"You must be ravenous after all that exercise," she said, bustling about.

"Binnie, you have the sight," quipped Angus, pushing the plate towards Nicola.

"Not me," the housekeeper declared. "I'm not one for seeing things. Not like Old Mairi."

"What is 'the sight'?" Nicola asked. "Is it fortune-telling?"

"In a way," said Angus. "But no crystal balls or palms needed. Old Mairi just has visions, sometimes not very clear, sometimes cryptic, and not to order. And she doesn't always remember afterwards everything she saw."

Nicola said slowly, "I met an old woman on the road here who was very strange. She was droving sheep."

Angus nodded. "That'd be Old Mairi." He raised an eyebrow. "Don't tell me she told your fortune."

"I asked her if I was on the right road for Craigie Moor," Nicola answered, "and she said yes. But she seemed to go into a kind of trance for a few moments. I thought she was going to have an epileptic fit. She was muttering, but I couldn't understand most of it."

Angus and Binnie Ross exchanged looks, and Binnie said, "The MacTavishes have been blessed, or cursed if you like, with the sight for generations."

Afterwards Nicola wondered why she had kept what she had understood of the old woman's strange words to herself. Because she might have sounded foolish, she supposed, and they might have given way to teasing speculation, especially concerning the bit about not returning. That had almost been fulfilled up there on the mountain today, she thought with a shudder.

Mrs. Ross said, as though she were glad to change the subject, "Well, now, Miss Sharman, did you have a good look at the eagles? You can tell me all about it while

Angus telephones Rowena to see if she can come and look after things until Morag is better.'' She glanced pointedly at Angus, clearly anxious to have the matter settled.

Angus didn't move. He bit into another scone and said, ''No point. I remembered that Rowena is in Inverness this week at some conference or other. She won't be back yet.'' The housekeeper looked dismayed, but Angus was unperturbed. ''It doesn't matter. You can still enjoy your cruise, Binnie. Miss Sharman will fill in for you until Morag can come.''

Mrs. Ross looked as astonished as Nicola. ''Miss Sharman! But—''

''I've invited her to stay and bird-watch on the estate for a few days,'' Angus said in a casual voice, ''and I'm sure she won't mind sparing a little time to help out until Morag's fit.'' He glanced questioningly at Nicola, casually confident, it seemed, of her agreement.

Nicola found it hard not to smile in triumph. ''No, of course not,'' she said. ''I'd be glad to.'' This was what had been in his mind all along, she thought, and the invitation to stay and bird-watch had been because he thought she might refuse. In a way, he'd conned her. If he only knew how he'd played right into her hands.

To Nicola's relief, Mrs. Ross seemed to approve. ''I'm very grateful to you, Miss Sharman.''

Angus said, in mock seriousness, ''Perhaps, Binnie, since Nicola will have no one to chaperon her, you'd better reassure her that I'm an honourable man.''

Mrs. Ross answered eagerly, ''Indeed he is, Miss Sharman. There's no finer gentleman than—''

Angus cut her off. ''Now, Binnie, there's no need to lay it on with a trowel.''

''Are you sure you don't mind?'' Binnie asked Nicola anxiously.

Nicola said, "I'm delighted to be able to repay Mr. Macpherson's kind hospitality, Mrs. Ross." She shot Angus a look, but the grey eyes weren't directed at her.

Binnie heaved a sigh of relief, and her anxious frown vanished. "Well, I'll be able to enjoy myself a lot better, knowing there's someone to look after everything. Men get in such a muddle in the kitchen." Angus laughed, but she ignored the interruption and said warmly, "I'm glad you can stay, lassie. It's a load off my mind."

Nicola was thanking her lucky stars that she hadn't impetuously succumbed to the temptation to reveal to Angus who she was. She was more than sure that she wouldn't be staying if she had, however useful she might have been.

"I'm glad you can stay, too," said Angus, a shade laconically, and the look he gave her made her knees quake more than the whole day's hill climbing had, and she felt giddier than she had been on the mountaintop.

CHAPTER FOUR

UPSTAIRS in her room, Nicola combed the tangles out of her windswept hair, but was less successful in unravelling the tangle of her emotions.

Keep it professional, she cautioned herself firmly. Don't get involved.

She still found it incredible that things had worked out to her advantage, after all; that she still had a chance of getting the Magnus Lord story, even if it was a pretty slim chance. "Please let him come back before Morag does," she pleaded silently. If Magnus Lord didn't return while she was at Craigmoor House, she would abandon the story. And let Hugh say what he liked! She had a few things she wanted to say to *him*, anyway.

Thinking of Hugh Vanter roused her anger and also feelings of disbelief that she had ever admired the man. "He's a ratbag," she declared vehemently. "No, not really," she amended honestly. Hugh was just a very good managing editor who believed that all was fair in love and journalism. Nothing had happened except that she had realised he wasn't the kind of man she admired, and that was because she'd met someone who was.... Her thoughts switched to dreamy recollections of Angus Macpherson's magical kiss, and she pulled herself up sharply.

Nicola Sharman, go and have a bath and get things into proper perspective, she advised her reflection, as she slammed the brush down on the dressing table and jumped up.

After a warm, relaxing bath, which did wonders for her aching body if less than she had hoped for her perspective, Nicola changed into a dark green sweater and tartan trousers. She shaped her eyebrows and lightly pencilled them, brushed a little powder across her cheeks, which still glowed from exposure to the brisk mountain air, and lightly coloured her lips with a pale orange-brown lipstick.

When she went downstairs a few minutes later, Angus was crossing the hall and stopped to speak to her. He had changed, too. A black polo-necked sweater and black corduroy trousers that moulded his broad, muscular frame, together with his dark colouring and his controlled but perfectly coordinated movements, made her think of a panther on the prowl. A fairly gentle panther, she told herself with an inward smile. At least, sometimes.

He said, looking steadily at her, ''Thanks for agreeing to fill the gap.''

''I could hardly refuse.''

He touched her shoulder lightly. ''You could have done, if you'd wanted to.''

''Could I? You knew I wouldn't say no to Binnie, didn't you? That's why you waited until we got back to mention it. And you bribed me first with an invitation to bird-watch!''

He smiled, saying nothing. There was a pause of only seconds, but it seemed to go on forever, his eyes boring into hers, until he said, ''I won't be too hard on you, I promise, and Binnie's done enough baking to see out a siege, I'll warrant.'' He took his hand away quickly, as though touching her had been a mistake.

''I was just going to have a few words with her,'' Nicola said. ''I expect she'll have some instructions for me. Is she in the kitchen?''

"Yes, I think so." As she turned away, he said, "You might as well come along for the ride to Fort William."

Nicola grinned. "Why? Are you afraid I might change my mind and leave you to cook your own breakfast?"

"You wouldn't be so cruel."

"You said you could fend for yourself."

"I didn't say I would enjoy doing it."

How much would he enjoy having her to look after him, Nicola wondered, or would anyone at all have done? Her blood warmed as she recalled how extraordinarily happy she had been up on the mountain with him; how utterly safe she'd felt when she was afraid, just because he was there. But she mustn't start getting ideas about him. He was a million miles out of her reach, even if he was as attracted to her as she was to him, and she was sure he was not.

Angus consulted his watch. "We'll be leaving in about an hour."

Binnie Ross was still pottering in the kitchen when Nicola entered. She confirmed Angus's prediction about the food situation.

"Ye'll not need to cook much for a day or two," she said, opening the refrigerator. "I've left you a couple of casseroles and a pie, as well as some puddings you'll just need to heat up." She showed Nicola the well-stocked vegetable racks and the larder where the rest of the food-stuffs she might need were stored.

"These are the flour bins," she said, indicating two large containers. "Ye might like to try your hand at baps—he likes them fresh. I'll leave you the recipe. And one for oatcakes, too."

"What are baps?" Nicola asked.

Mrs. Ross smiled. "Ach, they're just soft bread rolls. Verra easy to make."

Nicola crossed her fingers. As a cook she was compe-tent enough, but not, she suspected, up to Mrs. Ross's standards. However, her efforts were bound to be better than what Angus would expect of a spoilt little rich girl.

They went back to the kitchen. "There's not a great deal to do here," the housekeeper reassured her. "A lot of rooms have been shut up because they're not used nowadays. Just keep the sitting room, drawing room and dining room vacuumed and dusted and the fire going in the sitting room while it's still chilly. The laird likes a fire there, even though we've got the central heating."

"And Mr. Macpherson enjoys his home comforts, too, no doubt," commented Nicola, smiling.

Mrs. Ross seemed to need to give the matter consideration before she said, "Ach, aye, they're a good pair."

"Doesn't Lord Kilgarrin employ any other staff?" Nicola enquired.

Mrs. Ross shook her head. "Nay. There's no need, and in any case it's difficult to get reliable domestics nowadays, especially in such an isolated spot. Morag comes up twice a year to clean right through or if we need help for a dinner party, which is rare indeed, but otherwise, despite its size, it's an easy enough house to run." She drew breath. "The laird likes his own company best and he doesn't entertain much. Lord Lachlan and his daughter, Lady Catriona, and the McAllisters are about the only regular visitors here these days." She added in a tone that sounded almost like disapproval, "Of course if he marries Lady Catriona, it'll be parties all the time whether he likes it or not, and the whole place will be done over." She paused and sniffed to convey her disdain.

Nicola was immediately alert. "Is Lord Kilgarrin getting married?" she asked interestedly.

"I said if," replied Mrs. Ross with another sniff. "I doubt if he's popped the question yet. *She* couldna keep it to herself if he had. But Catriona Lachlan is a very spoilt young woman who believes she ought to have everything she wants. And she wants Magnus." She clucked, this time with definite disapproval. "It's her father's fault. Mind you, she's a beauty, gypsy dark like her mother, but with bonny blue eyes. Lady Lachlan died when Catriona was a wee bairn. There are no sons so it's not surprising Lord Lachlan, who's a good bit older than his wife was, is keen for his daughter to marry Magnus, what with the estates adjoining."

Nicola was tempted to risk a few more questions, but the housekeeper was anxious to finish her packing and said so, apologising as she hurried away.

Mrs. Ross's train left on time and Angus and Nicola saw her safely onto it with her luggage and wished her a happy holiday. Binnie wiped away a surreptitious tear and promised to send postcards, and once more rather anxiously said she hoped they would be able to manage.

"We will, but only just," said Angus tactfully. "So don't you dare elope with the first millionaire you meet." He kissed her cheek fondly and then the whistle blew and the train moved off. As they watched it disappear down the line, he said, "Binnie can't bear to be away from Craigmoor House. The only way her sister could be sure she won't rush back after two days was to make her take a cruise. And you wouldn't believe the trouble we had persuading her to go."

"That's wonderful loyalty," said Nicola. "Lord Kilgarrin must be a nice man," she added, "to inspire such devotion."

Angus laughed. "I daresay he could rob and murder and she'd still stick up for him."

Nicola was reminded of the mystery surrounding the death of Magnus Lord's wife, and she wondered again if there was anything in the rumours that had circulated at the time.

There was a chill wind blowing and Nicola shivered, partly because of it, partly because of her thoughts.

Angus put his arm around her shoulders. "Come on. It'll be warmer in the car."

It was—luxuriously warm—and although Angus made only token conversation, mainly to draw her attention to points of interest, Nicola felt relaxed with him, and the prospect of spending the next few days at Craigmoor House was a pleasurable one, quite apart from the story she might get.

It was dark when they arrived back and the lights they had left burning in the house glowed invitingly through the undrawn curtains. Rolf gave them a vociferous welcome, and a few minutes later Nicola was busy in the kitchen. She finished cooking the dish Mrs. Ross had left in the oven and turned on the hot plates under the pans of vegetables. The table in the dining room was already set. Binnie Ross was a meticulous housekeeper and there was very little else for Nicola to do, so when Angus invited her to join him in the sitting room for a drink, she accepted.

"Whisky again?" he asked temptingly.

"If it's that wonderful malt stuff you gave me before."

"You'd better not develop too great a fondness for it."

"I won't. I'm not really much of a drinker." She added teasingly, "You can mark the level on the label if you're afraid I'll tipple when your back's turned."

He laughed. "I've got better things to do than distrust you."

Nicola felt a sharp pang of guilt and a deep sense of frustration. Oh, why couldn't she have met this man in nice, normal circumstances? She couldn't help giving a little sigh. In normal circumstances, her path and Angus's would never have crossed; she didn't number Scottish lords or their estate managers among her friends and acquaintances.

"What's the matter?"

"Matter?"

"You sighed. You're not regretting what you've taken on, I hope."

"Of course not." Nicola took a sip of whisky and let its mellow warmth trickle through her. Then she said, "I was just thinking, it must be a big job running an estate as large as Craigmoor."

"It keeps us busy. But Craigmoor isn't as big as some. Lord Lachlan's place, which adjoins Craigmoor, is twice the size. Although I daresay the two together wouldn't compare with some of your smaller sheep stations."

"Will they amalgamate?"

He was clearly taken aback. "I shouldn't think so. I was only making a comparison."

Nicola was tempted to take a chance. "I only wondered because Mrs. Ross said Lord Kilgarrin might be going to marry Lady Catriona Lachlan."

A fleeting expression of annoyance crossed his face, but he merely said, "There are always rumours. The gossips have to have something to gossip about."

"Lady Catriona is young and beautiful, so Mrs. Ross says, and the merger of two aristocratic families would seem to be logical," Nicola ventured.

"Is logic a basis for marriage?" he challenged.

"In some circumstances it might be."

"Would you marry a man your father chose for you, just because it would seal an advantageous business deal?"

Nicola grinned. "That would depend on the man. So long as he was good-looking, rich and considerate—"

"What about love?"

Nicola pretended indifference. "You can't always have everything."

To her surprise he looked angry. "If you're so cynical about marriage, you'll soon find out how wrong you are and live to regret it. Marrying for the wrong reasons brings its own retribution.''

Nicola was caught by a wave of remorse. She had unwittingly touched a raw nerve. Angus Macpherson had been hurt. A failed marriage, perhaps. She longed to know about it, to show her sympathy and understanding, but dared not probe. She wished she hadn't been flippant, and tried to make amends.

''I would only marry a man I loved,'' she said, looking him candidly in the eye.

He turned away and poured himself another drink. Hers was scarcely touched, so he didn't offer her more. ''Is there one?'' he asked, not turning round.

''I thought there was,'' she answered honestly. ''But I realised my mistake. If I'd married him it would have been for the wrong reasons, like you said.''

He whipped round, half smiling, and looked relieved. ''I'm glad to hear it.''

But he didn't mean that personally, Nicola thought. He just didn't want anyone to make the same mistakes he'd evidently made. She said slowly, ''I'm sure you've given Lord Kilgarrin the same advice as me, and perhaps he'll take it. Do you think he might be in love with Lady Catriona?''

Angus pulled a face. ''I daresay the matchmakers believe he is.''

''And Lady Catriona might have reason to.''

''Or she might not.''

''You haven't heard from him yet, I suppose,'' Nicola ventured, adding by way of explanation, ''I'd like to know if I'm going to be catering for two or three.''

''No, I haven't heard from him,'' Angus said. ''I probably won't. He doesn't have to tell me what he's doing.''

Like Binnie Ross, he was very loyal to his employer, Nicola reflected as she dished up their meal. She had quite forgiven Angus for railing at her yesterday—without any right to be angry in the first place, she thought guiltily. His suspicions had been justified, after all. How she wished they hadn't been!

Over dinner, the conversation was mainly about eagles and the work of the estate. Nicola had some anxious moments when Angus switched the conversation to her and asked about her background, but she kept to facts as much as she could, embellishing them a little to fit the previous image she had created. Her father, she thought once with amusement, would have a fit if he knew how she had described him, giving the impression he owned a chain of hotels, not one modest motel.

To Nicola's surprise, Angus assisted in carrying the plates out to the kitchen when they had finished, and began to stack the dishwasher.

"You don't have to help," she protested.

"Just making sure you get the hang of things," he said wickedly.

She retorted in mock indignation, "You think I don't even know how to work a dishwasher?"

He gave her a teasing look. "I'm sure you're very talented in many ways." Mockery edged his words as he said, "Let's see how you cope with the coffee maker."

"If you go and sit down by the fire, I'm sure I'll cope beautifully."

"Oh, yes, beautifully, to be sure," he murmured, the teasing look not quite gone from his grey-blue eyes, which skimmed pointedly over her.

Nicola felt more disconcerted by him than she was prepared to admit. Her skin seemed to tingle from his very presence, and as she waited for the coffee to drip, she warned herself to be careful. Reacting to a man the way she was reacting to Angus was highly dangerous, and she'd better remember it. She was here in this house for professional journalistic purposes only. Personal involvement was out.

Fortified by her own sensible advice, she carried the tray with coffeepot, cups and plate of shortbread resolutely into the sitting room, and nearly dropped it when she saw Angus lounging against the vast mantelpiece, staring into the fire. He hadn't seemed to hear her come in, and the expression on his face, in profile, was so revealing, she ached unbearably for him. Their earlier conversation had obviously raised memories of past hurts. It touched her deeply to find that under his seemingly imperturbable exterior, the man was vulnerable.

Her hands shook, making the cups rattle, and he looked up, his expression changing instantly. "Let me." He crossed swiftly and took the tray, placing it on the table in front of the couch.

Nicola poured the coffee and he sat beside her, leaning back in a relaxed fashion, his hands behind his head. When she stifled a yawn, he gave her a smiling look.

"You must be worn-out with all that climbing. I should have an early night, if I were you."

"I'm not really tired. It's just so lovely and warm and relaxing here." She caught another yawn behind her hand, and he laughed.

"Well, you're not obliged to entertain me all evening," he said. "I'll be off to attend to some paperwork as soon as I've had coffee. So you can have your early night."

Nicola felt subtly rebuffed. What he really meant was that she needn't expect him to entertain her just because he'd invited her to stay around and bird-watch, and pay for the privilege with a bit of housekeeping.

She didn't let her disappointment show. "I suppose, with Lord Kilgarrin away, you have quite a lot extra to attend to," she said, adding, "If you need any letters typed, I can do them for you."

"Thank you for offering, but I don't expect that will be necessary."

When he had drained his second cup, Angus rose and asked her to excuse him. Nicola went back to the kitchen, cleared the dishwasher and then checked the food situation again, detailing in her mind how she would arrange meals tomorrow. She spent a few minutes perusing the recipes the housekeeper had left her, and decided that baps did sound easy to make. She would surprise Angus with a batch in the morning.

Later, as she went quietly upstairs, she noticed that there was a light under a door that led off the hall. Presumably it was Magnus Lord's study and Angus was working there, catching up on the estate work she had prevented him from doing today.

She went to bed, still thinking of the unexpected vulnerability she had surprised in him and wondering who could have hurt him, and why. Perhaps his own suffering had contributed to his fiercely protective attitude towards Magnus Lord's privacy. She fell asleep, still wondering futilely about this complex man whom she had no chance of ever getting to know well.

Despite her preoccupation with Angus Macpherson, Nicola slept soundly and woke stiff and aching from her previous day's exercise. A hot bath relieved some of the tension in her muscles, and by the time she had dressed in blue jeans and a white cowl-neck sweater, she felt more normal.

Although it was earlier than she was accustomed to rising, a warm teapot on the kitchen table testified that Angus had been up before her. She poured fresh hot water on the leaves and drank a cup herself before setting two places at the table and putting the porridge on to cook. A few minutes later Angus came in, rubbing his hands together.

"Good morning, Nicola. How are you?" He was brisk and impersonal today, and scarcely looked at her. The affability was still there, but it almost seemed that he had decided not to be too friendly. If she hadn't seen the evidence of it with her own eyes, Nicola would not have believed now, any more than she would have believed it at their first encounter, that he was vulnerable.

"I'm very fit, thank you," she answered, feeling ashamed of the involuntary thought that it would be delicious to be enveloped again in those strong arms and crushed against that warm, solid body. She said quickly, "Porridge won't be long."

He leaned against the edge of the kitchen table, long legs extended, arms folded across his chest. He was in her way, and Nicola had to keep passing him as she went about preparing breakfast.

"I didn't expect you to get up so early," he said. The grey eyes were teasing, and his manner seemed to soften as he added, "No ill effects from yesterday?"

She dragged her eyes away from his mouth. Fancy wanting a man to kiss you at this time of the day. A faint blush crept into her cheeks. If he guessed what was in her mind, she'd *die*!

"I've got a few aches," she admitted, going back to the stove to stir the porridge. "I guess I used a few muscles I haven't exercised for a while and some I didn't even know existed."

He eyed her sternly. "You should have told me you suffered from vertigo."

"And miss seeing the eagles? It wasn't so bad, really."

"It damn well was, and you know it. You were terrified. Don't ever be so foolish again. It's not your fault you can't stand heights. You don't have to risk your neck to prove you're brave."

Nicola lifted the porridge saucepan off the stove and carried it to the table. Angus shifted into a chair, managing to brush close to her as he did so, and the casual contact made her hand shake so much that when she ladled out the steaming oatmeal, she spilled some on the tablecloth. As she wiped it up, Angus remarked, "I didn't think spoilt little rich girls were so domestic."

"Then I'm surprised you risked asking me to housekeep for you."

He looked steadily at her. "I'm sorry. It's mean to tease you. I take it all back." His eyes drifted across her face, studying her, and then he went on, "I'm still not quite sure what to make of you, Nicola Sharman. Somehow I get the feeling there's more to you than meets the eye."

Nicola swallowed hard. He mustn't start getting suspicious again. "You make me sound intriguing, like I'm some kind of Mata Hari."

"She was a spy."

Nicola raised her eyebrows. "Is there anything to spy on here?"

"Magnus."

Nicola didn't have to feign impatience, and it covered her underlying uneasiness. "I thought we'd settled that."

He lifted a hand. "Yes. Yes, I'm sorry. I'm paranoid, I know."

"An occupational hazard with bodyguards, I suppose."

"You could be right."

Nicola took the opportunity of a slight pause to switch the subject. "Is it cold out today?"

Angus sprinkled salt on his porridge. "No, it's quite mild, but Jock says there's going to be a change in the weather shortly. He reckons it'll snow within the week."

"Who is Jock?"

A grin broke out on his face. "Craigmoor's *gillie*, I suppose you could say."

Nicola blushed.

"He lives in quarters over the big barn," Angus told her, "and his forecasts are always more accurate than the weather bureau."

"Isn't it a bit late for snow?"

"Not here. I've known snow on the hills in July." His expression was serious. "It's not ideal weather for lambs, of course. A snowdrift isn't the best place to enter the world in."

"Is it lambing time now?" Nicola asked.

He chuckled, not too unkindly, at her ignorance. "I suspect you know as much about nature as a sheep knows about public relations. It's spring, lassie, and in spring— well, I guess you know what generally happens in nature in spring, don't you?"

After that he was silent, and Nicola didn't attempt to make small talk. Her thoughts wandered. If she were at home in her Sydney apartment now, she reflected, she would be having a much less leisurely breakfast, probably grabbing a piece of toast and a cup of black coffee. And most other meals would be from take-aways or in restaurants. She didn't often cook for herself, but she enjoyed giving small dinner parties for friends from time to time.

After breakfast Angus disappeared and Nicola settled down to her chores. She decided to mix some dough for an experimental batch of baps, then make the beds, clean out the sitting room grate and set a new fire before vacuuming.

Nicola was enjoying the pleasure of rhythmically kneading a soft dough when there was a loud rap at the back door. It was a man delivering milk and cream and fresh vegetables, who regarded Nicola with interest.

"Good-day to ye, lassie. You're the wee Australian bird-watcher, I ken. Heard about ye in the *clachan*. Good of ye to help out while Morag's sick." Striding past Nicola along the passage to the kitchen, he called over his shoulder, "I'm Archie McClintoch. I'll put the box on the kitchen table for ye. Everything Binnie ordered is there."

Nicola followed meekly and was treated to another curious examination before he left. "Aye," he said consideringly, "ye're a bonny lass, all right. Old Mairi wasna seeing things all the time." He added, "Just give us a call if you need anything else, Miss Sharman. I can bring it up for ye. Cheerio now."

Nicola set her rolls in a warm place to rise, then put away the provisions Archie McClintoch had brought. By the time she had done that and one or two other small chores, the baps were ready for the oven, so she decided to leave the beds and do the downstairs rooms first. She was on her hands and knees cleaning out the grate in the sitting room when Angus reappeared.

"There you are! Good grief, girl, what are you doing?"

"Nothing, I mean I'm cleaning out the grate." She stood up, pushing stray strands of hair off her face.

Angus burst out laughing. "And you seem to have transferred most of the soot to your face, Cinderella." He pulled out a large white handkerchief and dabbed at a patch on her cheek.

"Leave it, there's no need to dirty your handkerchief," Nicola said hastily. "I'll go upstairs and wash it off." His nearness was beginning to disturb her more than she cared to admit.

He tilted his large frame back to study her. "You look like an urchin. A very appealing little urchin." Abruptly his amusement was replaced by a different look, and his arms slipped around her. As their lips met, Nicola trembled like a girl receiving her first kiss. He lifted her chin and smiled into her eyes. "The trouble with you, Nicola, is that you're too kissable to resist."

"Stop it, Angus, please," she murmured.

Long, sensitive fingers stroked her cheek. "Do you really want me to?"

If he'd decided not to be too friendly, he wasn't being very conscientious about it, Nicola thought. She stretched her head away from him with an effort. A little breathlessly, she said, "Yes, I do." But the trouble was she didn't.

She struggled out of his grasp and turned her back on him. "Go away, Angus, and find something useful to do. I didn't agree to stay and help out just so you could fool around with me." Obviously she'd been mistaken about his slightly offhand manner when he'd first come into the kitchen that morning—although kissing hardly came under the heading hospitality.

"I came in for morning tea," he said, eyes twinkling. "There's a wonderful aroma of fresh bread in the kitchen."

"My baps!" Nicola fled, quite forgetting the sooty smears on her face, and certain that her first attempt at bread baking would be a dismal failure and that Angus would laugh at her. The timer pinged as she reached the oven. She was gazing triumphantly at her handiwork when Angus came in and perched on the corner of the table.

"Perfect," he said, reaching for one and breaking it open.

"They're hot. You'll burn yourself," she warned.

"I like 'em fresh," he retorted with a grin, and placed the two steaming halves on the table.

By the time Nicola had made coffee, his bap was cool enough to eat and he did so, pronouncing it excellent. He eyed her wickedly. "If perchance Binnie does meet a millionaire on her cruise, I might consider offering you a permanent position."

"Lord Kilgarrin might not approve of your choice," Nicola suggested lightly.

Angus chuckled. "Oh, I don't think he'd object. I usually engage any staff we require." He gave her a long, steady look, drank his coffee and added, "I could always marry you, I suppose, to be sure."

"I thought you didn't approve of marriages of convenience," Nicola reminded him tartly.

His eyes were twinkling. "Oh, you never know. We might eventually fall in love."

"You flatter yourself. But thanks for the compliment, anyway."

He was only teasing her, Nicola knew, but he didn't know how close to the bone it was. She was reminded all too painfully of Hugh Vanter and his offer of marriage to persuade her to do what he wanted. She wouldn't get caught like that again. What Angus had said wasn't the same, but she felt let down. Did all men think marriage was the ultimate prize every woman wanted?

"I've offended you." Angus's fingers were tilting her chin and he was looking anxiously into her eyes. "Haven't I?"

"Of course not." She felt foolish and confused.

"I have. I can see it in your face. I'm sorry. I don't know why I'm tempted to goad you."

"Because you're an arrogant male," she chided.

"And because I have the oddest sensation that you're one up on me," he said thoughtfully, "but I don't know why."

"Maybe we should both just get on with our work," Nicola suggested, jerking away from him.

"You're right. I'll try to be nicer at lunchtime."

Nicola couldn't help laughing at his expression of contrition. But after he'd left her, she almost wanted to cry. The man was getting to her in all sorts of indefinable ways, and she wasn't as in control of herself as she would have liked to be.

She finished cleaning out the grate in the sitting room in a rather sombre mood, and it wasn't until later when she went upstairs to make the beds that she glanced in the mirror and saw the soot marks down both cheeks and a smear on the end of her nose. No wonder Angus had been looking so amused all the time they were having coffee. She looked an absolute clown!

After she had tidied her own room, she went along the passage to do his. The first room she looked in was obviously unoccupied, as the bed was untouched. It was a large, bright room, very masculine in décor and she decided at once that this must be Lord Kilgarrin's bedroom. Feeling she was prying, she closed the door hastily and further along found a room that was plainly Angus's temporary accommodation. It had the air of having his belongings hastily thrown into it.

Because she couldn't help feeling like an intruder, Nicola worked quickly, darting nervous glances at the door as though she were afraid Angus might appear at any moment and tell her she had no business there, even though he surely expected her to clean the rooms. There was something disconcertingly intimate about making his bed. He had expensive taste in night attire, she noticed as she folded silk pyjamas and hung up a velvet dressing gown. She wasn't surprised: Angus struck her as being a man who would always choose quality rather than quantity.

She had lunch ready to serve when he walked in at twelve-thirty, and was gratified by the look of appreciation that lit his face because she hadn't kept him waiting.

"Binnie would be dismayed to see how little she's being missed," he commented.

"Thanks for the compliment, but be sure you tell her it was terrible without her," cautioned Nicola. "She'll expect it." She grinned at him. "And wait till we've used up all the food she left and you have to rely entirely on my cooking. You might change your tune then."

"Nothing wrong with your baps," he said. And then, "What do you plan to do this afternoon? There's no need to slave in the house all day."

Nicola had already decided. "I thought I'd go down by the loch," she said. "I noticed a lot of water birds there yesterday." This wasn't entirely for effect. She really was developing a fascination for birds since Angus had talked to her about them and shown her the eagles.

He nodded approval. "Go wherever you like, Nicola."

There was no reason why he should have joined her— he had work to do, after all—but during the afternoon Nicola caught herself longing for his company in a vague, unsettling way, constantly glancing over her shoulder to see if he had suddenly appeared, and being disappointed when he didn't. Sitting quietly by the tranquil loch, raising her binoculars occasionally to observe a bird on the water or in the still, leafless trees along its edge, she nevertheless felt unusually content. *Private Lives* magazine, Hugh Vanter and Maynah Grimes all seemed a galaxy away. Her thoughts drifted to Magnus Lord from time to time, and gazing out across the loch, she wondered about the death of his wife. Had it really been an accident, or had the rumours to the contrary been based on fact? And if she did eventually meet Magnus Lord, would she have the nerve to ask him? Or would he peremptorily throw her out as Angus had said he would?

As she dabbled a stick in the water that gently lapped the shoreline by her feet, she began to wonder for the first time if she was really cut out to be a journalist, after all. Hugh had told her often, and Maynah, too, that she

needed toughening up; that if she wanted to reach the
top, she must learn to put the story first, herself and everyone else second. But did she really want to reach the
top? Would being an editor at *Private Lives* really be as
satisfying as she'd once believed? Self-doubt had never
bothered her before, but suddenly she seemed able to see
through people like Hugh, and even through herself. It
was unnerving.

"Keep your mind on the job," she chided herself, "and
stop getting sidetracked." The trouble was she had no job
to do now, and unless Magnus Lord returned soon, she
would never have one. It was the uncertainty of it all that
was getting to her, she decided finally.

CHAPTER FIVE

ALTHOUGH Nicola was up very early next morning, she was still later than Angus, as the warm teapot on the kitchen table confirmed. She was stirring the porridge when he strode through the kitchen door with Rolf at his heels. His hair was tousled and there were bits of straw sticking out of it. He had obviously been doing some task in the barn. He looked at her for a long moment before he said, "Good morning," and when he smiled warmly, Nicola felt as though the sun had just broken through the mist.

"Good morning. Breakfast's ready," she announced. "Are you?"

"My stomach is," he rejoined, disappearing into the scullery to wash his hands.

Rolf lay down by the stove and, tongue lolling, looked expectantly at Nicola. She fed him and then ladled out porridge for Angus and herself.

"Looks like being a fine day," he remarked. "The mist is rising already."

"I hope so," said Nicola. "But I thought you said Jock had forecast snow." She slid two slices of bread into the toaster.

"That's his long-range forecast," Angus said. "Like old Mairi MacTavish, he has the sight; but being a man, it's limited—weather only."

Nicola asked seriously, "Do you believe in it? 'The sight,' I mean. Can some people really see things that will happen in the future?"

Angus shrugged. "Nobody around here would take what Old Mairi sees lightly."

"Has she ever seen anything of your future?"

For a fraction of an instant, his face clouded as though with some unwelcome memory, but he answered flippantly, "Not what I'd like her to see—fame, fortune and beautiful women."

The toast popped up, and Nicola transferred both slices to Angus's plate. He was already slicing the top off his boiled egg and didn't speak again until he'd finished, when he startled Nicola by saying, "Your next destination was Skye, I believe you said?"

"Yes." Nicola looked away quickly, but he must have noticed that she was watching him.

"We'll take a run over there today," he stated. "And as it's fine, we might as well take a picnic and eat out-of-doors."

"You don't have to feel obliged to take me sight-seeing," Nicola protested.

His mouth quirked a little. "Are you getting bored with my company?"

"I'm not easily bored," she retorted, thinking that he was probably the most interesting man she'd ever met, even when he was saying nothing at all. He always seemed to be giving her something to think about.

"Good. Skye is one of my favourite places," he said. "And I haven't been over for a while."

They left soon after breakfast, leaving a disappointed Rolf behind. Nicola had urged Angus to let the dog come. She wasn't so wary of the Great Dane now; in fact, she was beginning to develop a fondness for him. But Angus had said, "It'd be too far."

"Oh, why?" she'd asked. "Does he get carsick?"

He had just grinned at her and said enigmatically, "You'll see."

It didn't take long to reach the Kyle of Lochalsh where they waited briefly for the car ferry, which transported them across to the Isle of Skye. It was a short, calm crossing to Kyleakin and there were few passengers. Nicola, with Angus standing close by, one hand resting lightly on her shoulder, leaned on the rail and absorbed the scene with real enjoyment. Sweeping her binoculars from time to time across the water, she observed a variety of seabirds that Angus identified for her, and as her knowledge increased so did her pleasure. Again she accepted his guidance when taking photographs, recognising his advice as that of an expert, even if he wasn't a professional. Magnus Lord's expertise with cameras must have rubbed off on him, as had his interest in ornithology.

"Skye is a large island," Angus told her as they settled back into the car on the other side. "You can't possibly see it all in a day, so you'll have to come back again if the place appeals to you."

"What are we going to do today?" Nicola's green eyes sparkled with expectation. She felt lighthearted and completely relaxed with Angus. She almost believed she was getting to know him, but stopped short of this presumption. She doubted if anyone would ever know this intriguing man well. Probably, she thought prosaically, that was what made him so tantalisingly attractive.

"You'll see," he murmured cryptically again.

What Angus had in store for her turned out to be the last thing Nicola had expected. After pausing for coffee in Portree, the island's chief town, which nestled picturesquely in the lap of a bay full of fishing boats and yachts and other small craft, they got into the car again.

When they stopped at a garage, Nicola glanced at Angus questioningly. The beautiful countryside was already beckoning to her and she could tell from the fuel gauge that they didn't need petrol. He had filled the tank in Kyleakin anyway.

"Why are we stopping here?" Nicola asked.

He regarded her with a deadpan expression. "You can ride a bicycle, I presume?"

Nicola's eyebrows rose in surprise. "Ye-es. But it's been rather a long time."

"You never forget," he assured her confidently. "Come on, get out. This is as far as we go by car."

As Nicola slammed the passenger door, she saw the sign: Bicycles For Hire. Angus was already striding towards a man who had strolled out of the office to greet him. From the cheery way they spoke and shook hands, it was obvious they knew each other well. Nicola took a deep breath of the sweet-smelling country air and steeled herself for what she feared was bound to be an ordeal. But there was no way she would let Angus think it wasn't the treat he obviously intended it to be.

The garage proprietor was wheeling out a bicycle and within minutes Nicola found herself reluctantly entertaining the men as she tested her ability. To her relief it was as Angus had said. She hadn't forgotten how to keep her balance. After five minutes' practice and some cheering by her audience, she felt reasonably competent, and as she dismounted Angus clapped her on the shoulder and said: "There, didn't I tell you?"

"I bet you really expected me to fall off."

He rumpled her hair in what was almost an affectionate gesture and then stowed the bag containing their lunch in the basket on his bicycle. He adjusted his trouser clips and mounted. "Follow me."

Nicola fastened her own trouser clips and shifted her backpack so that it sat comfortably on her shoulders. She had to pedal furiously to catch up with Angus, who was setting a spanking pace. After riding alongside him for a mile or so, she gave up the unequal contest. Let him wait for her, she thought, and reduced speed so she could enjoy the scenery.

With a sparkling blue sky lightly feathered with clouds above her, rolling fields on either side, the sombre grey Cuillin Hills a jagged line on the horizon, and pine forests clothing the nearer hills, it was a peaceful scene and she felt carefree and contented despite the thought of her masquerade.

Black-faced Highland sheep proved to be something of a hazard, however. They started up suddenly from the roadside, sometimes dashing across in front of the bicycle, and she had one or two near misses. Once she almost skidded into the roadside ditch, which was dangerously concealed by grass and other vegetation.

She saw few birds. Even when she had a long view ahead, Angus was nowhere to be seen, and Nicola felt mildly piqued that he had deserted her so readily. Finally she encountered a hill that defeated her. Despite the six gears on her bicycle, she was forced to dismount and walk up.

At the top, sitting on a boulder at the edge of the road, Angus was waiting. Nicola's heart gave a lurch and she sharply drew in what little breath she had left. Was she completely mad? she wondered, letting this man get to her so easily? So he was handsome, had extraordinarily compelling eyes and a tantalising if rather rare smile; he wasn't the only man on earth with such physical endowments. What it was that was unique about him, Nicola couldn't define.

"I thought you must have given up and gone home," he teased.

"When you've got the lunch?" she retorted breathlessly, joining him on his perch.

"Which we're not going to have until we get to Bracadale." He draped an arm across her shoulders in a friendly gesture.

"Is that far?" The warmth Nicola felt didn't come from energetic cycling.

"It's on the other side of the island. But don't worry, you're doing splendidly. We'll get there before we starve." Then, eyeing her steadily, he said, "Of course if you feel you can't make it, we can go back now."

Nicola had no more intention of giving in here than she had on the mountain above Craigmoor House. "I always finish what I start," she said.

"Yes, I reckon you probably do," he murmured and let his hand fall back to resting on the boulder.

He allowed her a few minutes' rest and then they set off again. Nicola's knees were beginning to feel like jelly despite the rest, and as she pedalled along beside Angus, who didn't race ahead this time, she couldn't help thinking that the further they went, the further it would be to ride back. Every pleasure had its price, she thought ruefully.

Presently, ahead of them, she glimpsed water and soon they were coasting down to Bracadale, a small village on the shore of the sea-loch.

"Are we there?" Nicola shouted across the freshening wind.

"Yes. We'll stop for lunch shortly."

When the road flattened out, Nicola had the sensation that her legs were pedalling of their own volition and there was no longer any proper feeling in them. She was also very hungry. The exercise and the cool wind had sharpened her appetite, and she was delighted when Angus called a halt.

They left the bikes leaning against a fence and trudged across a field to the stark ruins of what must once have been a crofter's cottage. The crumbling stone walls were overgrown with moss, and every crack sprouted weeds.

Beyond the sea-loch the rugged Cuillins dominated the skyline. All around the wild, rocky shoreline, gulls wheeled and screamed, and the sea sprayed up over the rocks. Behind them lay scattered farmhouses, and their entry into the field was noted by some sheep who briefly lifted their heads to stare at the intruders.

"Let's sit on the wall," Angus suggested and, clasping his hands firmly around Nicola's waist, he hoisted her up. As he set her safely on top, their eyes met for a moment and Nicola's composure suffered a severe disruption. She was shocked to find herself wondering whether he would mind if she leaned forward just a little and placed her mouth on his. His hands seemed to linger for just a fraction of time longer than necessary. Could he be having a similar thought? If he was, he didn't translate it into action.

Nicola lifted a leg over to straddle the wall, and seeing she was secure, Angus let go. "Thanks," she said, hoping he was unaware of her palpitations.

He leaped up beside her, placing the lunch bag between them. "Tea first. I'm parched." He began to unscrew the top of a thermos.

Nicola gulped her tea down thirstily, too. The sandwiches were quickly demolished, followed by fruit and the rest of the tea. Nicola repacked the bag with a sigh of satisfaction.

"I thought you expected me to do that," Angus said, grinning at her. "I thought your motto was Fair Division of Labour."

"Oh, I'm not rigid. I don't mind letting a man feel superior now and then," she joked, and he laughed with her.

But suddenly Angus stopped smiling, and the look he was giving her confused her so much she fumbled and the bag fell off the wall. She swung herself over, intending to jump down, but he jumped off the wall first. He held out his arms to her and then for a moment everything went into slow motion. His hands clasped her waist and purposefully he pulled her down into his arms, folding them tightly around her and crushing a startled gasp from her before his mouth brushed tentatively across hers.

There was a dreamlike quality about the way she yielded to his embrace. His lips fluttered over her closed eyelids, nibbled her earlobes, traced the sinews of her neck and then skimmed back to her willing, waiting mouth. His long fingers threaded caressingly through her hair, removing the restraining band that held it in a ponytail and letting the silky tresses run through his fingers as he lightly massaged the nape of her neck.

"You certainly don't look or act like a hard-bitten lady journalist," he murmured, catching her hair in both hands and lifting it. "I can't think why I thought you might be." He wasn't just trying to convince himself. He was sure now, and his certainty was altering his view of her, he realised. This fragile, warmly vibrant woman who had slipped so unexpectedly and dramatically into his life was changing everything—including, if he wasn't careful, himself. But he mustn't let it happen.

There was a catch in Nicola's throat. A wave of guilt made her swallow hard and painfully. "You mean, I do look like a bird-watcher?" she eventually managed to say lightly.

His gaze drifted caressingly across her face, and with a touch that tingled, he tucked a stray strand of hair behind her ear, his fingertips spreading wildfire to every corner of her being. His voice was husky when he said, "No. You simply look quite delicious with your hair all windblown, and your cheeks flushed and your eyes sparkling." The grey eyes weren't teasing now; they quite openly and naturally expressed his feelings. "You look quite enchanting and frankly, Nicola, at this moment, I don't give a damn who or what you are."

Angus bent his head and kissed her again, long and passionately this time, until she felt her whole body melting against his in a way that had never happened before. The sound of the ocean rose to a crescendo in her ears and the shrill cries of seabirds only added to the primitive rhythm of the passion to which they were both succumbing.

It was a shock when Angus abruptly released her and said with a look that startled her with its intensity, ''I'm going for a walk.'' He picked up his binoculars, slinging the strap over his head, and marched off.

''Crazy,'' he muttered out of Nicola's hearing. ''You're crazy! Stop giving the poor girl ideas.'' He tramped over the first rise. What was the matter with him? This wasn't what he wanted. A woman, yes—it wasn't a sin to desire a beautiful woman who felt warm and pliant and willing in your arms—but not an involvement. He must keep his feelings well and truly clear of that kind of danger.

Nicola was hurt by his rejection and regretted showing so warm a response. She must have frightened him off by appearing to be too eager, she thought. But she hadn't been able to help it. She leaned against the wall and watched him go. She felt guilty. She had allowed something strong to happen between them in the past minutes that she shouldn't have. But she couldn't have stopped it, she thought helplessly. And now, obviously he was wishing he had. ''Damn!'' she exclaimed on a sob of disappointment. Now the day was spoiled.

She watched his dark silhouette move against the bright sky as he walked towards the edge of the sea-loch. He paused briefly on a crest of land above the rocky shore, then vanished down the other side. As he disappeared from view, warm tears slid down Nicola's cheeks, but she didn't know why she was so moved. She took a deep breath and flicked the tears away. What sort of man was this that he could make her cry? She hardly knew him, and yet . . .

A few moments later, he came into view again, further along the black, rocky shore. He stopped and lifted his binoculars to watch a seabird wing its way across the wide expanse of the bay. Taking up her own binoculars, Nicola watched the bird's flight too until it disappeared. Then she swept her glasses around the bay. Magnified, the distant Cuillins seemed even more stark and forbidding, and the sea looked dark and treacherous out beyond the headland.

Nicola lowered her binoculars and looked at the shoreline, inevitably catching Angus in her field of vision. Her heart lurched as he loomed suddenly large, seeming so close while actually far away. He was standing with his back to her, long legs firmly apart, powerful shoulders thrown back, still intently watching something far out to sea. Nicola couldn't tear her gaze away from him. She was transfixed by the intimate-yet-distant view. It seemed to say everything about the man: however close you might come to him physically, the real Angus would remain at a safe distance.

As though he sensed her scrutiny, he suddenly turned and focused briefly on her. Seeing that she was watching him, he waved and, she thought, beckoned to her. When Nicola, pretending she hadn't been staring, failed to respond, he repeated the wave, emphatically jerking his head in a gesture that confirmed that he wanted her to join him.

She abandoned her pretence, and with an extraordinary glow of pleasure and relief, ran through the grass and clumps of pink sea thrift towards him. She was breathless when she reached him, but as lit up inside as though someone had pressed a switch. The thought that it was Angus who was responsible for this radiance was alarming, but inescapable.

"What is it?" she asked breathlessly.

He caught hold of her arm, instantly making her heart beat faster. "Look, out there on the water." He pointed across the bay while Nicola vainly tried to pick up what he was pointing at. "Guillemots," Angus told her, "and puffins. You can't see them too clearly because of the sun glinting on the water."

"I can't see *anything*."

"Here, try mine." Angus offered his more powerful binoculars. He slipped the strap over her head, his casual touch making her hands shake so that focussing was difficult. With the greater magnification she was eventually able to see the two species of bird and pick out the gaily striped beaks of the comical puffins.

"I've always wanted to see them!" she exclaimed, and that, she thought gratefully, wasn't an act. "I've only seen pictures of them before." Her eyes were sparkling with a delight that owed as much to Angus's nearness as to the birds when she looked up into his face.

He was standing behind her and suddenly he folded his arms around her and pulled her gently back against him until she was leaning against his hard muscular chest. Surprised, she turned her head away quickly. She mustn't let him see how strongly he affected her. It was bad enough that he had to feel the runaway beating of her heart.

He didn't speak for some moments and the tension became almost unbearable, especially when he idly nuzzled his chin against her hair.

"Isn't it about time we started back?" she ventured at last.

His hands fell away from her, as though she'd wakened him from a dream. "I expect so," he said matter-of-factly, and as she turned round, added with a challenging smile, "How's your pedal power?"

"Just fine," she answered, although her knees threatened to buckle under her at the mere thought of riding all the way back to Portree.

He grasped her shoulders and looked deeply into her eyes. She thought he was going to kiss her again, but he didn't. He merely said in an exaggeratedly broad Scots accent, "You're a braw wee lassie, Nicola. Aye, that you are." And he laughed. It was a warm, affectionate sound that seemed to wrap right around her heart.

With his arm draped over her shoulders they walked back across the field to the road where they'd left their bikes. It occurred to Nicola that she had never felt so companionable with anyone before. If only they'd met in different circumstances, she began thinking again, and scolded herself for such foolishness. Her time with Angus would have to be cherished in memory alone.

By the time they had ridden back through Bracadale, the sun had disappeared behind a bank of clouds rolling in from the west and the wind was stronger and colder. Nicola pedalled gamely on, head bent, trying valiantly but unsuccessfully not to fill her mind with foolish fantasies.

Presently, as they pulled up at a passing-place to allow a string of cars to go by, it began to rain. Angus, turning up the collar of his jacket, glanced at Nicola ruefully. "This is all we need."

"End of a perfect day," she joked, turning her mouth down ironically, as she, too, pulled up her jacket collar.

"Was it?" he murmured. "Perfect?"

Nicola was in no doubt whatsoever. "Perfect." Her voice was husky, as though she were going to cry. How stupid can you get? she admonished herself, swallowing hard.

There was a long, supercharged moment, broken only when a van pulled up alongside them. "Like a lift?" offered the driver.

Angus didn't hesitate. "Yes, thanks."

He opened the passenger door and Nicola collapsed onto the seat with relief. How glad she was she didn't have to ride all the way back, after all, especially in the rain.

The driver of the van, an elderly farmer, doffed his tweed cap politely, then got out to help Angus stow the bicycles in the back. He and Angus chatted all the way to Portree about the weather and the prospects for the summer tourist trade. Nicola, squeezed between them, was aware only of Angus's closeness, of his shoulder and thigh in warm contact with hers, as her fantasies took flight once more.

By the time they reached Portree the rain had eased off. The van dropped them at the garage where they returned the bicycles and collected Angus's car.

"As it's so late, we might as well have dinner in Portree," Angus suggested as they drove back into the town.

Nicola surveyed herself doubtfully. "I'm not fit to be seen."

Angus gave her a swift glance. "You look all right to me, but you can have a wash and brush-up in the hotel if you want to."

He drove to the same place where they'd had coffee that morning and they dined in a pleasant restaurant overlooking the harbour. As darkness fell, lights on the boats anchored in the bay vied with the lights from the wharf that were luridly reflected in the dark, oily water. In his low, resonant voice, Angus regaled Nicola with stories of the island's history, and his account of the flight of Bonnie Prince Charlie to Skye, helped by the faithful and courageous Flora Macdonald after the Battle of Culloden, was as exciting as it was moving.

"It was a pity Charles didn't quite fulfil the Highlanders' faith in him," Angus said, as though he personally regretted it. "After the victory at Prestonpans they were cock-a-hoop with a prince, they said, who could 'eat a dry crust, sleep on pease straw, eat his dinner in four minutes, and win a battle in five.' Actually he took ten to win Prestonpans, and maybe that fluke went to his head because the Duke of Cumberland beat him easily at Culloden. He wandered for five months before escaping to Skye, disguised as an Irish spinning-maid, and then he went to France."

Nicola laughed. "I would like to have seen him in drag. I bet some of his men wouldn't have been too impressed."

"He was only twenty-five," Angus said, causing her eyebrows to rise in astonishment, "and Cumberland had his twenty-fourth birthday the day before Culloden."

"Victory was a nice present for him, then," Nicola said, "but didn't they call him the Butcher?"

"They did. He wasn't very merciful to captives."

Nicola shuddered. "It's fascinating, all that history, but I think I'd rather live in the twentieth century."

Nicola could have sat there all night, letting Angus's rich, deep-toned voice keep her spellbound, but finally he brought the magic to an end.

"Time to go if we're to catch the last ferry."

The journey back didn't seem to take as long as in the morning. Angus drove fast but competently and Nicola felt total confidence in him. Although she was tired, she didn't feel drowsy, but neither did she feel like talking. She just wanted to savour the day's special pleasures in her mind. Angus, too, seemed disinclined to chatter, so they drove most of the way in silence. He was a great talker when he had something to say, she mused, but he didn't bother with idle chat.

It was well after midnight when they reached the house. The night air was chill, but a welcome warmth enveloped them as they entered, and Rolf greeted them effusively, putting his front paws on Angus's shoulders as though they'd been away for days instead of hours. Nicola carried the picnic bag out to the kitchen, intending to wash out the thermos. Angus followed and took it out of her hand.

"I'll do that. You must be dead beat. Go up to bed."

Nicola didn't argue, knowing he would insist. "Thanks." She paused. "And thanks for today, Angus. It was marvellous. Good night."

"Good night, Nicola."

She was turning away when, as though impelled by an invisible force, Angus moved between her and the door. His hands on her shoulders detained her and the desire that had been kindling all day suddenly appeared as an urgent need in his grey eyes and tense fingers.

Alarmed, Nicola tried to draw back. But before she could speak he had slid his hands under her sweater, making contact with her bare skin. He clasped her around the waist, drawing her tightly against him, and there was nothing tentative about his kiss now. It conveyed all the pent-up emotion he had kept under tight rein today on the shore of the loch. Nicola felt herself falling, and spinning into a whirlpool of ecstasy that promised to transform her completely. Suddenly she knew what her crazy feelings were all about, what the conflict of joy and pain that was tearing her apart meant. She was falling in love with this man. What she felt for him wasn't just a passing infatuation; it had all the hallmarks of the real thing.

"Oh, God, please, no," she breathed silently. "It will hurt so much."

Some deep, mysterious part of her responded to him as to no other man she'd known, but the pleasure of her feelings was cancelled out by the pain of realising that if he knew the truth about her, he would despise her. She was attractive to him only because he believed she was as innocent as she pretended to be. And now she knew that she loved him, she also knew she must preserve that innocent image permanently. Even if Magnus Lord returned, she would not reveal herself. His story would never be written by her. It almost amused her to think of what Hugh would say if he knew how subjective she was being; but he never would know because she wasn't going to see Hugh Vanter or *Private Lives* ever again....

"Nicola." Angus's ragged breath warmly caressed her cheek and when he picked her up in his arms, she didn't protest. She let him carry her up the stairs, her head pressed deep into his shoulder as she breathed in the warm maleness of him, feeling her heart racing against the steady rhythm of his. He entered her room and tenderly set her down on the bed. Nicola involuntarily drew his head down close to hers.

"Angus." She threaded her fingers through his beard and hair, filled with an impossible longing—a longing for love that she would be unable to deny if he stayed with her, yet knowing it would be a love whose sweetness could linger only in memory.

He brushed her lips with his and teased the corners of her mouth, delighting in the eagerness with which she let herself be swept away by his probing kiss. In the end, however, it was he who suddenly disentangled himself from her arms.

His sanity returned in a rush. He'd gone too far. Although his whole being cried out for the fulfilment her soft, yielding body could give, he held back. She would be too easy to fall in love with. He looked down at her, still fighting with himself, and when she tried to drag him near again, he caught her two hands in his and held them tightly. He bent and briefly touched her lips with his. "Much as I would like to stay with you, Nicola, my sweet, I'm not going to—for a whole lot of reasons I can't even begin to explain and which you would never understand; but I assure you that one of them isn't that I don't want you."

"Angus," she whispered. "Don't leave me."

He said so softly that she wasn't sure she heard him properly, "I'm sorry, Nicola, but there is no permanent way for us; and I'm not going to let you persuade me to do something you might regret in the morning. Good night, lassie."

He stood for a moment looking down at her curled on the bed with her glossy brown hair tumbled in disarray about her face and shoulders and her green eyes pleading with him. Was it possible that she loved him? He hesitated, then stepped back. It made no difference. There could be no future for the two of them.

Nicola turned her face away from him. "Good night, Angus," she mumbled, her voice muffled by the pillow.

Because he couldn't help himself, he bent and touched his lips to the silky hair and stroked her head lightly. The glimpse he had of the bare, creamy flesh above the band of her trousers, and above it, her full, rounded breasts as revealed by the form-fitting sweater, was nearly his undoing. He had to force himself to straighten and leave quickly.

After he'd gone, Nicola stared vacantly into the emptiness of the room and wept for the foolishness of falling in love with a man like Angus Macpherson. She'd only known him for a few days. It was the craziest thing she'd ever done in her life. And she knew instinctively that as punishment for her foolishness, she would be haunted by him for a very long time....

CHAPTER SIX

WHEN Angus came in to breakfast next morning, Nicola felt too embarrassed to look at him. The emotional intensity of the previous night was still with her, and all her efforts to restore serenity crumbled the moment he entered the kitchen. She could only hope he would think that the colour surging into her face was caused by the heat from the stove. She couldn't help his knowing she was strongly attracted to him as a man, but he must never guess that her true feelings went so much deeper than mere physical longing.

"Good morning." She managed to sound normal as she darted a quick glance over her shoulder at him, taking care to avoid meeting his eyes directly.

Angus grunted, "Good morning." He sounded as though he, too, hadn't quite been able to shake off the after-effects of almost letting his emotions sweep out of control.

"It's still fine today," Nicola said, turning from the stove at last and forcing her voice to remain steady. "But colder, I think." Still not looking directly at him, she began to ladle out the porridge.

Angus hadn't yet sat down, and as she turned to hold the empty saucepan under the tap, she felt his arms fold around her waist. When his cheek rested against her hair, the blood began to pound in her veins and her mouth was dry as she swallowed nervously.

"I'm sorry about last night, Nicola," Angus said huskily.

His apology was unexpected. The saucepan clattered into the sink and she gripped the edge of the stainless-steel bowl tightly. Just what was he apologising for?

"'Sorry'?" she quavered. "I don't recall that you've anything to be sorry for." Unless it was leaving her, she thought wryly.

His breath stirred her hair and made her scalp tingle. He turned her round slowly, holding her arms firmly. "I have. For wanting to take advantage of you, for using your flattering response to me earlier in the day as a lever."

"But you didn't," Nicola said, with a lightness of tone not mirrored in her feelings.

"And so now you're feeling a bit guilty because you wanted me to."

Nicola tried to escape from him, but his arms continued to imprison her. "Of course I'm not," she muttered. "I'm just grateful I didn't have to fight you off."

He held her closer. "Nicola, you're not a very convincing deceiver. That's what I like about you; you let your feelings dictate your actions. You're open and honest."

For the next thirty seconds Nicola's tongue seemed stuck to the roof of her mouth. Finally she managed to say, "I thought you still had doubts about me."

He cupped her face in his large, warm hands, tilting her chin a little, and after gazing for a moment into her eyes, placed a kiss very lightly on her lips. Nicola tensed, yet quivered inside at the intimacy.

"None whatsoever, now. I guess I had become a bit paranoid, seeing reporters lurking behind every tree."

"Isn't that what good bodyguards should do?" she murmured. "It was wise of you to be suspicious of me."

"Nevertheless, I'm sorry."

"You don't have to keep apologising. I understand perfectly."

"Yes, you're a very understanding sort of person," he said, threading his fingers through her hair at her temples, "but there are some things that even you couldn't be expected to understand."

"Well, I don't understand what you mean by that, for a start."

"You don't need to," he answered slowly, brushing his lips across hers again.

"Angus, the porridge is getting cold," she muttered raggedly.

With a laugh, he released her. "If there's one thing I can't stand, it's cold porridge."

He flung himself down at the table while Nicola, with tremulous hands, put bread in the toaster. The world, which for a few moments had been slightly askew, reverted to normal—almost.

Nicola had little appetite for breakfast and ate desultorily, finding herself more interested in watching Angus finish his porridge, slice the top off his egg, butter his toast and spread it thickly with marmalade and drink his tea. She would sacrifice anything, she thought recklessly, to be allowed to enjoy the simple pleasure of watching him perform these small personal rituals every day of the rest of her life. She felt a tenderness towards this enigmatic man that astonished her.

All at once his every gesture was becoming achingly dear to her. It was as though there had been a void inside her that now had to be filled to overflowing with impressions and feelings—all of them engendered by Angus Macpherson.

She was still lost in her private world of painful contemplation when Angus asked, "No aches from your long ride yesterday?"

Nicola swivelled her shoulders. "I'm okay. A bit stiff, that's all."

He stood up and came round to her side of the table. He placed his hands on her shoulders and his strong fingers gently massaged, bringing not just relief to her muscles but a total feeling of well-being. Angus murmured, "Better?"

"Mmm, that's lovely." Revel in it, she told herself. Make the most of every moment. It won't last long.

Angus continued for a few moments to knead her shoulders in silence, then surprised her by saying, "If you like, I'll take you out on the loch today. We could go across to the island."

Nicola turned her head. "Really, Angus, you don't have to—"

Angus dug his thumbs deep into her shoulders, almost hurting. "Entertain you. I know I don't, but I thought you might enjoy it. The island is a veritable bird sanctuary." What on earth had possessed him to suggest another outing? he wondered. He ought to avoid being alone with her. "We might as well take lunch," he said recklessly. "And make the most of the fine weather."

"When are we going to get the snow that Jock promised? It couldn't look less like it at the moment," Nicola remarked.

"It'll come, don't worry. But not today."

"Well, if you're sure you're not neglecting Lord Kilgarrin's estate," Nicola said flippantly, "maybe when I've finished my chores—"

He stiffened a little. "You don't have to go if you'd rather not," he said. "I don't want to inflict myself on you. You can take the boat across yourself if you like."

"I don't know how to sail."

Angus's eyebrows rose. "You surprise me. Surely your father has a yacht?" A teasing look in the grey eyes softened the slightly scathing tone.

"No, he hasn't. His passion is flying." She didn't add, however, that he didn't own a plane, but flew with a club.

"I see. Do you fly, too?"

"No, it doesn't appeal to me."

"You don't get vertigo in a plane, do you?"

"No. But I like to have my feet very firmly planted on the ground most of the time."

"You don't mind water?"

Nicola said airily, "If you've got a motorboat, I could show you how I water-ski."

"No water-skis," Angus said regretfully. "But I'll teach you to sail, if you like. Living by that fabulous harbour of yours, you ought to have fallen out of your cradle into a boat."

Nicola laughed. "All right. I'm game."

The *Ealadh* was a smart little sailing dinghy and under Angus's expert tuition, Nicola quickly learned to crew for him. As with everything she did, she gave learning how to sail all her concentration, and Angus watched her with pleasure. The stiff breeze tossed the bouncy brown waves of her hair back from her smooth pale forehead, giving a new attractiveness to her delicately boned face that was pink with effort and alight with the pride of achievement.

As they tacked back and forth on the crossing to the small wooded island in the centre of the loch, Nicola had never felt happier. Love was not all sweet words and meaningful glances, she thought, nor was it all passion and sexual fulfilment; it was just being with someone whose personality fitted yours, who was the missing piece of your own personal jigsaw puzzle.

It felt so incredibly right laughing with Angus as he continued to teach her the rudiments of sailing, and pulling faces at him when he corrected her errors. Once, when she almost capsized the little craft and they rocked perilously, Angus's strong arm steadied her, his face came very close to hers and she longed for him to kiss her, but he didn't.

It was strange, she reflected, how love came slowly sometimes, out of a long and pleasant friendship, and how sometimes it was instantaneous. There seemed no rhyme or reason to it. There was certainly no logic in her having fallen in love with Angus Macpherson. A more unsuitable object for her affections could not exist. Looking at him, his yachting cap pushed rakishly back from his forehead, a lock of dark hair sweeping down to his eyebrows, she suddenly felt an almost overpowering urge to confess, whatever the consequences, but it was harder than ever now to turn her thoughts into words. She could not bear to spoil the magic.

Presently, as they walked up a steep, sandy path to the thickly wooded centre of the island, pushing through brambles and bushes that had overgrown the track, Angus caught hold of her hand in a perfectly natural way to help her along, but to Nicola his touch was like a trigger to her feelings.

It took only a few minutes to reach the highest point of the island, where they stopped by the ruins of an old stone cottage. There was a chimney still standing, with some cracks and crannies sprouting tufts of grass, weeds and delicate wildflowers. Around the ruins lay the remnants of stone walls, overgrown with gorse and nettles. Through the still-leafless trees, there was a commanding view of the loch and of Craigmoor House, which, flanked by woods and set against the backdrop of mountains, looked as picturesque as a postcard.

Nicola was poignantly reminded of the similar scene on Skye when they had lunched in the shelter of another derelict cottage. There had been a closeness between them then, a drawing together that had led inexorably to what had happened last night. But today wouldn't be the same. Angus had regained control of his emotions. She only wished *she* had. He still made every nerve in her body raw with wanting his arms to hold her, his lips to join with hers. . . .

Nicola moved away, pretending to admire the view. "What a marvellous vantage point!" she exclaimed, and looking around, added intuitively, "This is Magnus Lord's private retreat, isn't it?"

Angus smiled. "Don't worry, Magnus wouldn't mind our being here."

Nicola walked over to the ruins. "Scotland seems to be littered with the ruins of abandoned cottages."

"It's a tough life on a croft. Your livelihood is at the mercy of the elements. Young people nowadays can make a better living in the cities."

Nicola nodded in understanding. "Who used to live here, Angus?"

"A couple who worked on the estate. When they retired and left, nobody else wanted the place so it fell into ruin. It's been like this for twenty years or more."

"This was once a flower garden," Nicola said, stooping and pushing aside some brambles. "Look—freesias. And wallflowers just coming out."

"They're early," said Angus, "but it's very sheltered here, sunny even in winter. Strong winds blow up the loch from the sea at times, though."

Nicola picked a creamy flower and held it to her nose. "Mmm, lovely. Freesias always remind me of my grandmother's garden. She loved old-fashioned flowers because they have the sweetest perfumes."

Angus, aware that his heart was ruling his head again, and not caring, took the flower from her fingers and placed it behind her ear. Then he tilted her chin and kissed her. "And what would your old homespun granny say about that?" he whispered.

Nicola was spinning out of control. Instinctively, she had given herself up to the luxury of his caress and she needed a moment or two to regain her composure before she replied lightly, "Oh, Granny always used to say, 'kissing don't last; cookery do.'"

He tossed his head back and laughed, then said only half jokingly, "Since you excel in both, you'll have no problems."

Turning away from her, he spread the rug out on the ground in a spot that afforded the best view between the trees. They stretched out lazily on it. Angus, lounging back against the wall, folded his hands behind his head and seemed to Nicola to be perfectly at ease. A longing to reach out to him, to touch him even in a cursory way, almost overwhelmed her, and to suppress it she quickly set about unpacking the sandwiches and the thermos.

Presently, when they'd eaten, he swept the remains of their lunch to one side and moved closer. He slipped his arm around her shoulders, drawing her against him, and when Nicola lifted her face to smile at him, he dropped a kiss on her nose, then another on her mouth while his hand brushed lightly across her breast. Although she knew it would be wiser to pull away, Nicola couldn't bring herself to end this intimacy. It was Angus himself who stopped the moment from getting out of control.

"You're a tantalising woman," he murmured, smiling ruefully. "How any man can resist you . . ."

"Oh, they do," Nicola said. "All the time."

"Then I must be ultrasusceptible to your particular charms."

"But you're resisting me nonetheless," she pointed out lightly.

"You're offended?"

"No. Of course not."

He looked at her steadily for a moment, taking her hand and turning it in a slightly agitated manner. "Nicola, there are compelling reasons—" he shrugged in a helpless kind of way "—obstacles." And then, as though deliberately shaking off unwelcome thoughts, he changed the subject completely and started talking about birds.

For some time they watched whatever ones ventured across their field of vision, and Angus identified a number of species for Nicola. She found his expert knowledge fascinating; but then everything about this unusual man was fascinating.

They were finishing off the coffee when he began to ask her more probing questions about herself and her job and her family. Nicola answered as truthfully as she could, while still maintaining the fiction she had already created. Using all her interviewing expertise, she deftly lured him to other topics that were, while personal, less likely to give her away.

She felt rather wistful, though, when this led to discovering that they had many things in common. It didn't surprise her that Angus liked music and books and art, but she hadn't expected him to be a fan of silent movies, or to share with her personal quirks such as preferring worn, comfortable clothes, enjoying going barefoot, and liking to stay up all night just to see the sunrise.

"You can have a television set in your room if you want to watch the late movies from the comfort of your bed," Angus offered.

"Thanks, but I don't think I'd be able to keep awake."

"Am I tiring you out?" His glance was drily teasing.

"I'm always a sound sleeper, especially after lots of fresh air and exercise."

"And you must have an easy conscience."

Nicola flinched. If only she had! "I have a guilty conscience about taking you away from your duties. What if Lord Kilgarrin returned unexpectedly and caught you loafing on the island with a female tourist instead of patrolling the estate with Rolf, on the lookout for snoopers?" she asked, laughing.

His brows came together in a guarded look and she almost wished she hadn't made a joke of it. But he answered easily enough: "Oh, Magnus doesn't interfere with how I run things, and I doubt very much he'll be back today, anyway."

"Is that his real first name?" Nicola queried, in spite of herself.

"Yes, it is."

"You said he used the name Magnus Lord when he was in the film industry. What did he do?" Angus had refused to discuss his employer before and she expected he would do so now, but to her surprise he didn't clam up.

"He was a film cameraman."

"You mean he shot movies?" She managed to sound surprised as well as impressed.

"He was a cinematographer, yes." He smiled at her. "I daresay you will have seen some of his pictures. They turn up on television from time to time."

"Oh, really. Tell me some titles," Nicola said, automatically seeking information, even though she knew she'd never use it. She was interested in Magnus Lord for a different reason now; because he was Angus's employer and because their obviously close friendship intrigued her.

Angus reeled off a list of titles, some of which she already knew, and some of which she had indeed seen. She said daringly, "I remember *White Wedding*. It starred Jacynth Moore. She was wonderful. She died quite young, didn't she? When I watched the movie on television the programme note said it was a tragic accident." She added casually, "Did you know her?"

"Yes, I knew her. She was Magnus's wife," Angus said, startling Nicola, who had fully expected him to change the subject. He took her expression, however, to mean astonishment at what he had just told her.

"You mean she was Lady Kilgarrin?" Nicola said, carefully maintaining her pretence of ignorance.

"Yes."

"Why didn't he use his real name?" Nicola queried.

Angus didn't answer immediately, but finally said, "He wanted to succeed in his chosen career by virtue of his talent, not his title. Until he married Jacynth, very few people knew he had one."

"Was it a happy marriage?" Nicola ventured.

"At first. They were both very young, both rapidly climbing their respective career ladders. But they had stars in their eyes, I suppose, and sooner or later they had to come down to earth."

Nicola was astounded at his candour. It could only be because he trusted her implicitly now. She felt a wave of guilt as she asked, "What happened, Angus? How did she die?"

"She was drowned."

"Angus, how terrible."

"Yes, it was."

"Were you there?"

"Yes."

"I'm sorry, it's obviously painful for you. Let's not talk about it," Nicola said. "It's none of my business, anyway."

"You might as well hear the whole story," he said slowly, "or rather, the real one. The Press at the time printed some lurid lies."

Nicola caught her breath at the irony of it. She was going to hear the story she had come to the Highlands of Scotland to get but had decided to abandon.

"Still..." she began, wanting him to go on, but wanting to stop him, too. Supposing, after he had told her, he somehow found out about *her*? She had seen him once in a towering rage, and she couldn't face him again like that. Not now.

Their eyes met briefly, then Angus looked away. "I don't think Magnus would mind my telling you the truth," he said. "It all happened a long time ago."

Nicola swallowed hard. There was no need to panic. He couldn't find out about her. There was no way he could unless she gave herself away; and she would make sure she didn't do that. She wondered why he was suddenly so anxious to tell her about another man's tragedy, and as she looked at his rigid profile, seeing the almost imperceptible twitch at the corner of his mouth, she believed she knew. She had guessed that Angus had himself been hurt, and she sensed strongly that his trauma was bound up with Magnus Lord's. She was so deeply touched that he wanted to talk about it to her, that the tears welled up in her eyes. He didn't notice because he was looking intently out across the loch, and she didn't dare wipe the moisture away for fear of drawing attention to her emotions. So she blinked and swallowed and waited for him to begin.

"I think you're owed an explanation," Angus began so abruptly that Nicola, transfixed by his stillness and wondering if he had changed his mind, jumped. He glanced at her and smiled, then looked away again. "You asked me before why Magnus and I are so paranoid about journalists. Well, we're not—not completely paranoid, I mean. They really did harass him unmercifully at the time of his wife's death and used so many cruel innuendoes that he vowed never to speak to one of them again."

He turned to look at her intently and Nicola had the feeling for an appalling moment that he had seen through her and she was about to receive the full force of his scorn. But again he confounded her by saying, "It wasn't just the Press who condemned him; it was even people he'd thought were his friends. But it was the Press who tore him to shreds in public. Magnus never forgave them for that."

Nicola hardly dared meet his eyes, but he wouldn't have said this much if he still had been suspicious of her, she told herself.

"The Press can sometimes be cruel," she agreed quietly, overwhelmed with guilt, as though she personally had been responsible.

He said with a sting in his tone, "And none was crueller than certain brittle lady journalists who had lost one of their most prolific providers of gossip, the darling of all the publicists: Jacynth Moore."

"What did they say?" Nicola whispered.

"They said—oh, not in so many words, just by hints and innuendoes—that he'd killed her."

Hardly knowing she was going to say it, Nicola asked bluntly, "Did he?"

"No!" Angus's emphatic denial echoed around the ruins of the cottage, as a cloud briefly obscured the sun, settling a chill silence over them.

Nicola shut out the awful possibility that his denial raised in her mind. If Magnus Lord hadn't been responsible for his wife's death, had Angus? Was that the cause of his suffering? The immensity of such a possibility was so overwhelming, she couldn't speak.

Angus went on in a measured, matter-of-fact tone: "Magnus and Jacynth were on holiday up here, taking a break before she was to appear in a new film. He was shooting it, of course—she refused to have any other cinematographer on her films, even then...." He paused briefly, moistened his lips and then continued: "The marriage had been shaky for some time and they came here for privacy, to talk about it, whether to part or to try and patch things up. Jacynth was edgy and Magnus suspected that despite her denial, she was having another affair. They had a few rows over nothing, explosions set off spontaneously because their nerves were frayed and something had to relieve the mounting tension. Jacynth was drinking again, too, and Magnus was angry with her because she had deceived him over it. He was desperately anxious for her problem not to become public knowledge, and had taken her away to a special clinic in Europe, pretending it was a skiing holiday. But she was soon as bad as ever."

This was startling new information to Nicola. The Press cuttings she had read hadn't mentioned it, so either they were being kind to Jacynth or it had been a remarkably well-kept secret. "And he was worried it would affect her acting?" she murmured, almost afraid to speak unless she caused him to stop talking.

He glanced briefly at her again. "It was already beginning to show in small ways. As her husband and as a sensitive cameraman, he was naturally the first to notice. But it was only a matter of time before it would have become obvious. The director of her last film probably guessed, but said nothing even to Magnus." He turned a rather sad smile towards Nicola. "Everyone loved her, you see. She had such a sweet, charming personality on the surface, but underneath she was terribly insecure. It wasn't her fault. Not entirely. She was a victim of the system that makes stars out of young women who aren't always able to cope with it all. Magnus tried to help her, but he failed."

And maybe you tried and failed, too, Nicola thought, but didn't voice the thought. It must have been agony watching her destroy herself. "How did she come to drown?" she asked.

There was a lengthy silence before Angus finally went on in a very low voice, "It happened one morning when Jacynth had taken a boat across to this island. It was a new habit she had adopted, saying she wanted peace and quiet to study her script. But Magnus guessed she had another reason—she was secretly drinking again. She was halfway back when the engine blew up. Magnus, who was in the boat shed working on some sail repairs, heard the explosion and swam out to her, but he was too late. The blast from the explosion had hurled her into the water, and as she wasn't wearing a life jacket and was somewhat inebriated, she drowned.'' The last words came out in a rush and the anguish in his face told Nicola things she didn't want to know.

''And where were you?'' she asked quietly.

He didn't answer at once, but finally said, ''I heard the explosion and raced to the scene, too, but there was no way we could save her. Magnus tried to revive her, but it was no good.''

He had loved her, too, Nicola thought bleakly. Angus had loved his employer's wife—maybe had even been her lover—and he must have been as shattered as Magnus Lord by her death.

Angus's voice cut across her thoughts. ''Others came running, too, of course. Jock, some of the other workers who were nearby, Binnie—''

''Don't go on,'' Nicola suddenly begged. ''You don't have to.''

But Angus seemed compelled to tell it all. ''It wasn't long before there were rumours. Magnus's name was linked with a young up-and-coming actress, and it was said that the boat's engine may have been tampered with.''

''If it was all untrue, why didn't he sue?''

He looked sharply at her. ''Because he didn't, doesn't make him guilty.''

''No, of course not.''

''He didn't sue because that would have meant dragging Jacynth's private life through the media, tarnishing her image. The media and the public wanted to remember her as the sweet, innocent girl on the brink of womanhood that she portrayed in most of her films." He gave her a rueful look. "Even Magnus saw her like that—in the beginning. And in the end, he still wanted to protect her reputation."

"Naturally. He loved her."

Angus shook his head. "No. By then, she had drained him of all affection. He was merely sorry for her. Even if they'd had a reconciliation, it would have been a marriage in name only, a marriage propped up for the image makers. Jacynth's death ended all that and the Press, angry with Magnus because he didn't want to tell them all the intimate details they demanded, invented their own stories."

"You don't believe Magnus killed his wife, do you?" Nicola asked.

"No." He gave her a strange, penetrating look. "But perhaps you do?"

Nicola shook her head and said with genuine conviction. "No, I don't believe he killed her." And I don't believe you did, either, she wanted to add, ashamed of the momentary suspicion she had allowed into her mind. Angus, despite a volatile temperament that could erupt into fury, would never kill anyone, or anything, as he had once said to her. She knew in her heart that was true.

Angus gave a short, ironical laugh. "Why not? The circumstantial evidence is strong."

"You were there and you said he didn't. I believe you," Nicola said simply. "I think you're honest."

Angus's expression was part amazement, part gratitude. "That's a compliment I may not deserve."

After a lengthy silence, Nicola said, "I can understand why Magnus quit the film business, retired to his estate and reverted to being Lord Kilgarrin." She smiled a little shakily. "And I can understand why you were so angry when you found me trespassing."

"Am I forgiven?"

"Totally. Thank you for telling me, Angus," Nicola said quietly. "It's a tragic story." She longed to ask him if he, too, had loved Jacynth, but couldn't bring herself to do that. His face had as good as told her, anyway. She said, "I can understand why Magnus quit all those years ago, but it seems a shame that such a talent should be wasted."

"He couldn't go back to filmmaking. There are still too many who would delight in raking over the old ashes."

"In Hollywood, maybe, but surely there are other sorts of films he could make. Documentaries for television for instance, here in Scotland. Under his real name, perhaps. People might not readily connect Magnus Kilgarrin with Magnus Lord. You said he was interested in ornithology. Why doesn't he make a documentary on eagles—that would be wonderful." She stopped, wondering why she was so enthusiastic to see Magnus Lord revived. Perhaps because it would revive Angus, too. She was sure, now, that the trauma of Jacynth's death had affected both men so deeply, they had almost had equal reason to retire from the world. She wondered if Magnus knew that Angus had loved his wife.

Angus was looking at her thoughtfully. "I doubt if he'd have the nerve."

"Fifteen years is a long time," said Nicola. "I bet he yearns to get behind a camera again. He must. A man with a talent like that who knows what he can do must want to create. You ought to try and shake him up a bit, Angus. You've both been immured in memories and bitterness for too long." What am I doing, talking like this to him? she wondered, astonished at herself, expecting a sharp rebuke. It didn't come. He was still looking intently at her, probably not even listening, she decided.

"I'm sorry," she said. "It's none of my business."

Angus reached for her hand and lightly held it. "I wonder what Magnus would think of you," he murmured and laughed softly.

"Well, it doesn't look as though I'll get to meet him," Nicola said regretfully. Angus's story had rekindled her interest in the reclusive Lord Kilgarrin, ex-cinematographer, and she would dearly have loved to meet the man who inspired such obvious friendship and loyalty in his estate manager and his housekeeper.

Angus didn't answer. He clasped her fingers a little more tightly and she could feel that he was going to draw her close. Suddenly the thought of being in his arms, knowing what she now knew, was too poignant. She withdrew her hand and hurriedly stood up.

"I think we should be getting back, Angus. I—I just want to pick a few freesias to cheer up the house."

She left him to fold the blanket and hoist the picnic basket on his broad shoulders, and when he set off back down the track to the landing stage, she followed a short distance behind him, wanting to be alone with her thoughts for a few moments. The impact of Angus's story about Magnus Lord's marriage was still mind-shattering, but although she had immense sympathy for Magnus himself, her heart ached more for Angus, whose anguish, she realised, was in some ways greater, because it was tinged with real guilt. It explained partly his intense loyalty to Magnus, to whom he must have felt the need to make some reparation.

As soon as they arrived back at the house, Angus went out again almost immediately, on some business about the estate, he told Nicola. She arranged the freesias in two small vases, one for the dining table, one for the sitting room. Their perfume pervaded the house and the splashes of colour brought a breath of spring-time indoors.

She was peeling potatoes for dinner when the telephone rang. As Angus was still out, Nicola answered it.

"Hello, is that you, Morag?" A lilting female Scots voice greeted her.

"I'm sorry, Morag is ill with flu," Nicola said. Before she could explain who she was, the other voice interrupted curiously.

"Who are you, then? You sound Australian."

"I am," Nicola replied. "I just happened to be here when Mrs. Ross was about to go on holiday and Morag was taken ill. I was able to stay and help out for a few days."

"You're a friend of Magnus's?" The caller sounded surprised.

"No, I'm just a tourist who happened to wander onto the estate, bird-watching," Nicola told her. It sounded a very unlikely story and the caller could be excused for thinking she was really a burglar. She'll probably call the police, Nicola thought with mingled amusement and alarm.

"Bird-watching!" the caller exclaimed. "How extraordinary. Oh, well, that's right up Magnus's street. Is he there?"

"No, I'm afraid not. He's—"

"Never mind, I don't need to speak to him. I just called to tell him that I've managed to persuade the Inverness contractor that the alterations to The Rowans will definitely be finished in time for the wedding—which is more than Angus managed to do. And a representative will be getting in touch in a few days."

"Wedding?" Nicola heard herself echoing.

"Yes. In June. For a while it looked as though Angus and I would have no home to go to, but that's all sorted out now." She paused for a microsecond. "By the way, what's your name?"

Nicola hardly had enough breath to say, "Nicola Sharman."

"How do you do? I'm Rowena McAllister. Hope to meet you before you go, and I must go myself right this minute. There's a car horn tooting for me. It's the local Conservation Council meeting tonight. Tell Magnus I'll give him a full report on it later, as I promised. 'Bye."

Nicola replaced the receiver slowly and carefully, although she wanted to crash it down in a fury.

CHAPTER SEVEN

NICOLA sat on the telephone stool with her head in her hands. How dared he? Angus Macpherson was engaged to be married to Rowena McAllister. And he had trifled with her, Nicola, as though it didn't matter. But it didn't matter, not to her, anyway. She was just glad she had found out.

She had told him she believed in Magnus's innocence because he did, and she believed he was honest. How he must have been laughing at her naïveté, playing on her obvious attraction to him, deceiving her all the time.

He hadn't let it go too far, of course. He hadn't actually been unfaithful to Rowena. He was just a casual flirt having a last fling before he got married, she thought bitterly. And she'd played along, boosting his ego for him.

She could hardly believe how wrong she'd been. It just didn't seem possible that the Angus Macpherson she had foolishly fallen in love with could behave in such a cavalier fashion. Nicola dismally concluded that never again would she be able to trust her judgement about anyone, especially a man. She was too easily conned. First Hugh Vanter, now Angus. What a fool she was, what a silly naïve fool, to have been taken in so easily. She had been sorry for Angus because he'd loved Jacynth, but doubtless he didn't deserve her sympathy. He was shallow and egotistical, and not the good friend Magnus Lord evidently believed him to be. And she was going to confront him and tell him exactly what she thought of his behaviour. She was not going to let him get away with humiliating her without some sort of redress.

This resolution made her feel marginally better, but when Angus came in to dinner, Nicola suddenly found she lacked the courage to remonstrate with him. When he came and put his arm around her shoulders and kissed the side of her neck, and his beard brushed tantalisingly across her cheek, she got so churned up inside, she could only draw away from him silently.

"Hmm, that smells good, whatever it is," he remarked, sniffing the air.

"Save your thanks for Mrs. Ross," Nicola said, more sharply than she had intended. "It's only one of her meals heated up."

At dinner she again meant to broach the subject of Rowena's phone call, but every time she opened her mouth, her courage deserted her once more. She was so afraid she would show the emotion she desperately wanted him never to suspect existed.

After dinner she pleaded exhaustion and said she would have an early night. Angus didn't try to dissuade her, but as she turned to go, he caught her firmly by the shoulders and turned her to face him.

"What's the matter, Nicola?"

Nicola avoided his eyes. "I'm tired."

"It's more than that, isn't it?" He drew her closer and she hated herself for the pleasure it gave her to be so near him. "Nicola, today, I don't know how to say this, but something has been happening between us, hasn't it? I'm sure you feel it as strongly as I do, and, well, before we go any further, there's something I must explain to you."

Nicola stiffened. He was going to do it for her. She felt suddenly that she couldn't bear it. "There's no need, Angus," she said coolly, "I already know. Rowena McAllister phoned earlier to tell Magnus that she'd sorted out the contractor who's renovating The Rowans and the house will be ready in time for your wedding, after all. I do think you might have mentioned that you have a fiancée.''

He looked thunderstruck, and ran his fingers agitatedly through his hair. ''Hell! Nicola—''

She knew she didn't have long before the strain would cause her to break down and she didn't want to weep in front of him. She cut across his words, hastily inventing another facet of her imaginary life. ''It doesn't matter, Angus. There's no need to apologise. It was a temporary thing, for both of us. A little bit of harmless deception. One thing I omitted to tell you was that I'm going to be married, too, to a man in Sydney. His name's Hugh—'' Her voice cracked ominously, and she caught her breath. ''My wedding isn't till July, though. A remarkable coincidence, isn't it?'' She pinned on a smile. ''You don't have to apologise for a harmless bit of flirtation. And don't worry, I won't tell Rowena if she comes over before I leave.''

''Are you serious?'' he asked, in a shocked tone.

''Of course I'm serious. Would you like me to fetch my engagement ring?'' She gambled that he wouldn't ask her to. ''I have it upstairs.''

''You said you were going to marry someone, but you'd changed your mind,'' he reminded her, looking perplexed.

''Actually, that was someone else,'' she said hastily, then added, ''It was a bit wicked of me to pretend I was fancy-free, I suppose, but when one's on holiday...'' She lifted her shoulders and stretched the smile a little. ''Stop worrying about it, Angus. I've just told you it's okay. We're both in the same boat. Nothing happened that either of us need be ashamed of.''

He still looked stricken. Perhaps he was afraid she would tell tales to Rowena, she thought. He said slowly, ''I'm not sure that's quite true—''

"Well, it doesn't matter. Let's just forget it ever happened," Nicola said, astonished at her ability to keep control of herself, after all. "And now, if you don't mind, I'm off to bed."

"Morag will be back in a couple of days," Angus said. "But if you'd rather leave before..."

Nicola would have liked to have run away right that minute, but that would only have shown him how upset she really was. And to leave in the morning would be nearly as bad. She had just pretended it didn't matter, so for the sake of her pride she would have to go on pretending that for another couple of days. No longer, please, she begged silently. I really won't be able to stand much more without cracking up.

She made a definite move to the door. "Good night, Angus."

"Good night, Nicola."

Facing Angus next morning was the hardest thing Nicola had ever had to do. She guessed it wouldn't be easy for him, either. He wasn't the kind of man who would relish having been caught out. He came in at the usual time, said good-morning, as she did, made some casual remark about the weather and sat down to his breakfast. Nothing was mentioned about the previous night. Angus ate his meal in silence, and Nicola didn't try to make conversation. There was nothing unusual about that, but on previous mornings, there hadn't been the same tension. It was a relief to Nicola when he went.

All she had to do, she told herself, was endure another couple of days. And so long as she focused on housework, cooking and bird-watching... Her mouth curved in an ironic smile as she listed the last occupation as something to concentrate on in order to avoid thinking about Angus.

Later in the morning, she was making a pie crust when he came into the kitchen. The pastry was bound to be awful, she thought. She was in no mood to achieve a light touch with it or with anything else, for that matter; but she needed plenty of activity to keep her mind occupied. She expected Angus merely to pass through, but to her surprise he perched on a corner of the table and watched her cut out the round of pastry and savagely crimp the edge. He sneaked a scrap of discarded dough and ate it with relish.

"You'll get indigestion," Nicola warned, her expression unsympathetic.

His eyes trapped hers for an instant, but there was no rapport between them now. They were strangers again, wary of each other, even antipathetic.

Nicola placed her pie in the oven and set the timer.

Angus slowly rolled another piece of dough between his fingers and formed it into a shape. He was acting like a man who had a lot to say but didn't know how to begin, Nicola thought. Still, she wouldn't encourage him. What was the point of an apology, anyway?

She wished Angus would go. She couldn't concentrate on what she was doing with him there distracting her. However, he seemed in no hurry to leave. There was a highly charged silence for another few moments while Nicola ran water into the mixing bowl and carefully wiped the marble pastry slab clean.

At last Angus spoke again. "Looks like Jock's forecast wasn't wrong. That's snow cloud building up, if I'm not mistaken."

"I hope it won't be heavy snow," Nicola said at once. "I don't want the rest of my trip spoiled."

"I'm sorry that part of it has been." His eyes locked with hers until she mustered the self-control to look away.

"I didn't mean that. I've—I've enjoyed staying here." She lifted her chin, hoping to convey that although she was angry with him for his deception, she was also quite indifferent.

"I've enjoyed having you here," he said, and actually sounded as though he meant it. "And very grateful, too."

"If it's likely to snow, I'm sure you must have a million things to do," Nicola said pointedly. "Would you like an early or late lunch?"

He stood up. "Better make it early. I'll be in at midday." He seemed on the point of leaving her, when he suddenly spun round and took a couple of strides across the room to bring him close to her. Heedless of her muffled protest, he whirled her into his arms, crushed her hard against him, and buried his face in the top of her head.

"Nicola, Nicola..." The perfume of her hair, the warmth of her slim body pressed close to his, acted like a drug, intoxicating him, making him want more and more, even though he knew the bliss it engendered would be short-lived.

Nicola, her cheek pressed against his sweater, tasted the same brief ecstasy. Breathing in his warm, masculine scent which was mixed with a sweet tang from the earth, mountains and heather, she was speechless and so filled with loving that her arms went around him unthinkingly and held him tightly.

His lips wandered agitatedly through her tousled hair, half kissing, half murmuring. "Nicola, this is crazy. We've got to straighten things out. I'm not going to spend another night like the last one. I didn't get a wink of sleep, and I suspect you didn't, either."

He held her away from him, just far enough to be able to look darkly into her face for his answer. "I can see you didn't. And I know why. You love me, don't you? You must, because I love you desperately, so desperately nothing else matters and I'm not letting you leave here until you—"

"Angus, please, you're out of your mind," Nicola managed to say. "You're fantasising—"

He caught her to him again, with powerful arms that held her more tightly than before. "I am not fantasising," he said in heavy tones. "I know this has happened quickly, but that doesn't make it any the less real. We go together, Nicola, so perfectly I can hardly believe it, and if you leave me, you'll wrench my heart apart." He almost shook her as he said fiercely, "You can't still be in love with that man in Sydney. Not now, Nicola—*not now*."

"Are you trying to tell me you're no longer in love with Rowena?" Nicola moistened her lips nervously. "That you would cancel the wedding because of me?"

Angus let her go quite suddenly and turned away. "It's not quite as simple as that. I've got a fair bit of explaining to do, Nicola."

"You would have. To Rowena, not to me," she said drily to his hunched shoulders.

He wheeled round, and the grey eyes were pleading. "First, just tell me that you'd cancel your wedding for me."

Nicola covered her face with her hands, knowing it was impossible. For one wild moment, however, she was tempted to confess her deception about Hugh, and to keep the rest of her secret—forever. But it was still true that if Angus was in love with her, it was the fictional woman he'd fallen for, not the real Nicola Sharman. But she couldn't live an untruth, not even for this man who had let her glimpse what love could really mean, and who had, almost overnight, changed her life completely. Lasting love required that there be no secrets between lovers. But if she told him the whole truth now, that would change everything. She could see the fire dying in his eyes, the incredulity entering his face, and then the fury that her deception would surely ignite. Wasn't it better to leave him to his Rowena, and perhaps keep a small place in his heart, rather than leave him with the sour taste of humiliation because he'd been duped? If only one could know in advance, she thought; if only one had the sight, like Mairi MacTavish, and could tell how another person would react, how genuine were their feelings, and whether what one chose to do was the right course.

Nicola decided. "The answer is no, Angus. I'm sorry. What flared up between us these past few days isn't enough. You're letting your passions run away with you." As you once did with Jacynth Moore, she thought sadly. "You love Rowena. You'll soon forget me."

He pulled her back into his arms. "I'll never forget you," he said, and joined his lips to hers with such an outpouring of need that Nicola was bewildered. Was it lack of warmth in Rowena that had made him turn to her so readily? Was marrying the brisk, friendly Scots girl merely a marriage of convenience although he had said he despised such arrangements? Was it because he had despaired of ever loving anyone as he had loved Jacynth Moore? A dozen crazy thoughts leaped through her mind and her heart ached for him.

"Nicola," he murmured at last, "I've got to go now, Jock'll be waiting for me, but this evening we'll talk about it again."

"No, Angus. There's nothing left to say."

He twirled a strand of her hair around his finger and yanked on it. "Yes, there is." And without another word, he strode out of the kitchen.

Nicola, drained of all sensible thoughts and emotions, continued with her chores, moving about the house like an automaton and asking herself all the time whether Angus could possibly love her and whether the love could sustain the confession she would have to make to test it.

He was going to talk to her again this evening, he had said. She would have to resolve her inner conflict by then.

It was almost lunchtime when Nicola stepped outside to place some rubbish in the garbage can and saw, with some surprise, a figure alighting from a bicycle, opening the gate to the yard and then remounting to cover the remaining distance to the house. Nicola recognised the cyclist instantly. There was no mistaking Old Mairi. As the old woman propped her ancient bicycle against the wall, Nicola went to meet her.

"Hello," she said cheerily. "You're Mairi MacTavish, aren't you?"

"Aye," agreed the old woman, shoving her hands into her capacious pockets. "Aye, that I am."

Nicola wondered what she had come for. She appeared to have brought nothing with her, but she must have cycled a considerable distance to get to Craigmoor House, which was miles from any other habitation, so presumably she had some specific purpose.

"Come in," Nicola invited. "Angus is out with Jock checking the lambs, and he'll be back soon."

Old Mairi did not reveal her errand, but merely followed Nicola into the house. She settled herself in a chair at the kitchen table as though she were accustomed to sitting there.

"Would you like a cup of tea or coffee?" Nicola offered, sensing that this was expected of her.

"I'd like a wee dram of Lord Kilgarrin's best malt whisky," said Old Mairi without batting an eyelid. She gave the impression that she really shouldn't have had to ask; that it was her due, normally paid without question.

Nicola hid a smile and fetched the drink. Then the old woman said, "I see ye've got the pot on the hob, so I will have some tea if ye dinna mind."

"Not at all," Nicola answered, pouring a cup and re-filling her own. Old Mairi fascinated her and she sat down at the table, prepared to ask a few questions if the old woman would let her.

Old Mairi took a swig of the whisky, then a sip of tea, and made a sound that conveyed satisfaction. Her pale blue eyes considered Nicola with the same unnerving intensity as they had a few days ago.

"I hope you don't mind my asking," Nicola said, "but I've heard that you have 'the sight,' that the gift has been in your family for generations."

"Aye, it has," said Mairi, bringing the whisky glass to her lips once more. "But sometimes it's more of a responsibility than a gift."

"Did you have a vision of some kind that day we met on the road?" Nicola asked. "You said some very strange things to me."

Old Mairi's weather-beaten features showed no emotion. "Not strange," she murmured. "Only what I saw."

"What *did* you see?" Nicola asked. "I didn't catch everything you said." She leaned forward eagerly, hoping the old woman would explain.

Old Mairi contemplated the dregs of whisky in her glass, then drained it. She placed the glass emphatically on the table and Nicola took the hint and fetched another "wee dram". Nicola was sure it was a long-observed ritual. When she returned, the old woman was sitting with her hands clasped on the table and she seemed to be in the same sort of trance as Nicola had witnessed before.

Nicola placed the glass in front of her, but she didn't appear to notice it. All at once her lips moved and the lilting Highland accent had the slightly blurred sound it had had the first time. But Nicola was more accustomed now to the Scottish burr, and her closer proximity to

Mairi allowed her to understand almost every word the old woman said.

"She doesn't know what to do. She's between the devil and the deep blue sea and she'll be in deeper water before she's finished with it."

"Who, Mairi?" Nicola asked quietly, hoping her voice would penetrate the trancelike state of her visitor. "Who are you seeing?"

As though she had heard the question, Old Mairi muttered, "The same, a woman, entering the house where he is waiting . . . from across the sea, never to return. They are both earthbound, but they are learning to fly, like the eagles. There is happiness, there is anger and recrimination and obstacles. The woman is leaving the house." The sonorous voice halted, and after a pause she said abruptly, "I can't see any more. It isn't clear any longer."

The sound of Rolf barking broke the spell and the old woman jerked back to reality, reached for the glass of whisky and finished it in one gulp, chasing the liquor down with the remains of her cup of tea.

"Who was the woman you saw, Mairi?" Nicola asked. "Was it me?"

Old Mairi looked at her for a long moment. "Aye, it was you."

"You saw me leaving this house?" Nicola prompted. "Is that what you meant by 'never to return'—that I would never come back here? Not that I would never return to Australia? Or is there something else that's going to happen to me that you haven't told me?" A shiver of apprehension accompanied Nicola's sudden new thought.

"It all depends."

"On what?"

"On yourself, lassie, of course."

"But if you can see the future, if the future is mapped out, it can't be changed, can it?"

"Not unless ye want to change it. What I see in the future is what will happen as a result of the present as it is now. If you alter the present, the future will change, too."

Nicola was mystified, but still curious. "What does it feel like, being able to see things?" she asked tentatively.

"It makes me tired."

"But you've always been able to do it? It just comes over you, like a sort of dream?"

Mairi looked a little perplexed at Nicola's analysing. "I have the sight, that's all I know."

"It's a very special gift," Nicola said.

To her surprise, Old Mairi shrugged. "We all have the sight, lassie, only most people don't pay any attention to it. We can all guess at the kind of future that will result from our actions in the present, but most people never do anything about it."

"I feel a bit like that," Nicola was surprised to hear herself confessing.

"Nay," the old shepherdess said. "You know where you're going and, God willing, you'll get there. Ye have the sight, lassie, so pay heed to it. Not to an old woman." She smiled—a slow, thoughtful smile—while looking steadily at Nicola. "Fate never takes unkindly to a helping hand, lassie."

"Would you like another tot of whisky?" Nicola offered.

Old Mairi rose. "No, thank ye. I must be on my way. I just came to pay the rent." She pulled an envelope out of her mackintosh pocket and laid it on the table. At Nicola's puzzled look, she explained, "I'm one of Lord Kilgarrin's tenant crofters, ye ken. And a fine, generous landlord the laird is. A true Highlander."

"Yes, I'm sure," Nicola murmured. "Thank you. I'll pass it over to Angus."

"He's a good laddie, too." The old woman shuffled to the door, chuckling for some reason.

Nicola watched Old Mairi mount the ancient bone shaker machine and ride off, none too steadily across the yard. She arrived at the gate at the same time as Angus and Jock. The three stopped and spoke for a few moments, and then Old Mairi moved off down the back road and disappeared around a copse of alders edging a stream. Angus and Jock strode together towards the house, Jock parting from Angus near the barn and Angus coming the rest of the way alone, a tall, compelling figure with a proud bearing, but, Nicola knew, still with the old wounds in his heart. It didn't matter now that he had deceived her. She wasn't even angry with him anymore. How could you be angry with the man you loved? Angus was merely human, as imperfect as she was herself.

"So you've had a visitor?" Angus said, breaking into her thoughts.

"Yes, she came to pay her rent."

"Never misses the day."

"She's a great admirer of the laird."

He smiled and eyed her speculatively. "I wonder if you would be, if Lord Kilgarrin could turn your head more easily than I do."

Nicola shrugged. "I daresay he wouldn't want to try." She turned and went swiftly into the house to avoid any further conversation along those lines, and Angus followed.

He didn't linger over lunch and was gone within the hour. It was a strain being in his company, with both of them trying to behave normally, but she missed him when he wasn't there.

It turned colder during the afternoon and the clouds seemed to settle lower and lower. The mountain peaks disappeared and the landscape took on a bleak look. Nicola was stoking up the fire in the sitting room late that afternoon when a large black car drew up outside the house. Peering through the half-drawn curtains, she found herself staring at the radiator grille of a Rolls-Royce.

Rowena? Nicola thought. Somehow she hadn't pictured, from the woman's voice, that she would own a status symbol like a Rolls. Angus didn't have one. And unless he was using it, neither did Magnus.

Magnus! Could it be Magnus returning? But he wouldn't park at the front of the house. Even as the thought was born, it died, because a small dark-haired girl in a green velvet jacket and tartan wool skirt got out of the car while a stout, rather florid man with a bald patch eased himself out on the other side. The girl was young, very pretty and had an air of affluence and authority. Aristocratic, Nicola thought wryly. She went to answer the clanging doorbell, consumed with curiosity.

"Good afternoon," she greeted them.

"Oh, hello," said the girl cheerfully in a barely accented but faintly regal tone. She flicked her deep blue eyes over Nicola. "You must be the domestic-cum-bird-watcher. Rowena McAllister told us about you." She tossed her dark hair and laughed, obviously highly amused.

The man also treated Nicola to a thorough appraisal. "Lachlan, m'dear. Lord Lachlan. This is my daughter, Catriona." He spoke in a broader accent.

"Oh." Nicola felt off-balance somehow, and even wondered for a fleeting moment if she ought to curtsey. She said, "Please, do come in. Is Angus expecting you?"

Father and daughter exchanged an amused glance. "We were just passing," said Lord Lachlan. "Just thought we'd drop in."

You didn't just pass Craigmoor House, Nicola knew. These people had come deliberately. Out of curiosity to see her?

"Angus is out somewhere on the estate," Nicola informed them. "If you'd like to come into the sitting room—I've just lit the fire in there—I'll see if I can find him."

Catriona swirled inside as though she were very familiar with the house. She held her slender white hands towards the fire. "Brrr. It's turned cold again this afternoon. We'll have snow, for sure."

Lord Lachlan dropped into an armchair, evidently also very much at home. As well both of them might be, Nicola was thinking, if Magnus Lord was really planning to marry Catriona. Maybe Binnie, who had told her that, knew more about it than Angus did. Magnus might well confide that kind of thing to her.

"Would you like some tea?" Nicola offered.

"I never say no to a cuppa," declared the earl, who seemed very easygoing and friendly. "Nice and strong if you will, lassie, and a wee dram wouldn't go amiss, either."

Catriona jumped up again. "Look, while you're getting the tea, I'll go and fetch Angus. Or send old Jock to find him." A sound made her turn. "Oh, there you are. You've saved me the trouble."

Angus was in the doorway and didn't look especially pleased to see his visitors, Nicola thought. She wondered if her offer of tea had been a little hasty.

"Lord Lachlan," Angus said, extending his hand. "Catriona." He cast an anxious look at Nicola as though he wished she would vanish.

She was about to when Catriona said, "I was talking to Rowena this morning, Angus, and she told me about Morag's flu and how lucky you were to be able to persuade Miss Sharman to stay and help out."

Nicola said, "Excuse me. I'll make the tea." She hurried out, hearing a peal of laughter from Catriona. The girl's ringing tones followed her across the hall. "Angus! What a joke. You are incorrigible. The poor girl! And you get free housekeeping in exchange for a bit of bird-watching."

Nicola gritted her teeth and didn't wait to hear any more. It occurred to her as she put the kettle on that Rowena may have asked Catriona to check out the situation before she herself descended on her fiancé. In the hope of catching him red-handed? Nicola would have laughed if she hadn't felt so dismal.

She cut cake and buttered scones, laid out shortbread and filled a small pot with jam, another with cream. She was about to carry the tray in when Angus appeared.

"I thought you might want a hand," he said, taking the tray and looking at her as though he wanted to kiss her.

She held the door open for him, then retreated to have her tea in peace in the kitchen. A moment later he was back, demanding that she join them in the sitting room.

"You're not a maid," he insisted roundly. "Come and have tea with us."

Wasn't she? Lady Catriona obviously regarded her as one. "No, really, I'd rather not."

He hauled her up. "They won't bite you. They're frightful snobs, but they're not bad sorts under all that. Catriona will need someone to talk to while I discuss a business matter with her father. Come on."

Nicola obeyed rather than create a scene. Lord Lachlan and his daughter showed polite curiosity about her and her travels and her interest in bird-watching, and Nicola strove valiantly to maintain her role. She was uncomfortably aware of their amusement, and of being treated as some kind of exotic novelty. Angus sat looking sardonic while they quizzed her, a finger lightly tapping the arm of his chair, betraying his impatience with the conversation. Presently he and Lord Lachlan left Nicola and

Catriona alone while they went into the study to discuss business.

"Daddy wants to buy a piece of Magnus's land," Catriona explained, "and Angus is driving a hard bargain." Her eyes sparked with amusement still, but the humour of the situation was beyond Nicola.

Catriona nibbled daintily at a piece of shortbread and surveyed Nicola with a sharp eye. Nicola remembered Binnie Ross's description of her as a beauty. Magnus Lord's housekeeper was right about that. *And* about Catriona being spoilt. He would have to relinquish more than a little of his privacy, Nicola suspected, if he married this girl. She wasn't the kind to hide her light under a bushel or in a Highland retreat.

Catriona's blunt remark regained her attention. "I hope you're not falling for Angus."

"I understand he's already engaged."

"Nevertheless, I wouldn't exactly blame you if you did," conceded Catriona, "because he's very handsome, and quite rich." She stopped as though she'd already given away too much about him.

"I had no idea he was rich," said Nicola, wondering how different her and Catriona's ideas of wealth would be. "And I suppose he might be quite good-looking under that beard."

"Don't you like it?"

"It's quite distinguished."

"I hate it. I shall make him shave it off," Lady Catriona said forthrightly.

"Maybe Rowena likes it," suggested Nicola gently, "which is what matters, surely."

For a moment Catriona seemed taken aback. "Rowena? Oh, yes, of course she has the last word with Angus." She laughed and then went on blithely, "It's a wonder she hasn't been round to scratch your eyes out." Catriona tilted her head slightly, giving Nicola a tiny but meaningful smile. "I wouldn't approve of the man I was going to marry living alone in the house with another woman." When Nicola didn't respond, she asked, "When is Morag coming to take over?"

"In a couple of days."

As she spoke, an outlandish but not improbable idea occurred to Nicola. What if Catriona was in love with Angus? She had looked at him with a somewhat predatory eye, Nicola now decided. Was she the jealous one? And was that because Angus had dallied with Catriona as he had with her? Was that the sort of man he was?

"Morag's a dear," Catriona said patronisingly, plainly relieved at the news. Her sharply inquisitive dark blue eyes showed, however, that she was still a shade uneasy about Nicola. Nicola was glad when, a few minutes later, Lord Lachlan and Angus came back.

"It's starting to snow," said Angus.

"Come on, Cat," urged Catriona's father. "We'd better be going."

Catriona gave Nicola a rather frosty look, obviously reluctant to leave her alone with Angus. Nicola accompanied Angus to the driveway to see them depart. As he'd said, it was snowing lightly, but flakes were building up on the gravel. The sky was leaden and the atmosphere cold and still. She shivered, and Angus instantly put his arm around her shoulders, a gesture she felt to be rather provocative in front of Catriona and her father, especially as Catriona would undoubtedly relay it to Rowena.

Catriona leaned out the car window and the blue eyes shot daggers at Nicola. "Goodbye," she said dismissively, then "*Au revoir*, Angus." Was the way she emphasised his name, and repeated it often, meant to underline their intimacy? Nicola wondered.

"Brrr, let's get back to the fire," Angus said as the car moved off, and with his arm still about her they ran back inside.

For Nicola the evening passed slowly in an atmosphere of tense uneasiness. She cooked dinner and served it and they talked desultorily during the meal, but it was obvious both their minds were occupied with private deliberations.

Over coffee in the sitting room, several times Angus seemed on the point of saying something, then changed his mind. He was clearly reluctant to carry out the promise he'd made earlier in the day. Eventually, when Nicola pleaded tiredness and rose to leave, he caught hold of her hand.

"Nicola, please, not just yet. Let's have a nightcap." He got up quickly and went to the drinks cabinet as though to ensure she would stay. "A small whisky—just to relax you."

She nodded mutely and sat down again. The fire suddenly seemed to crackle very loudly, hissing and spitting in the grate as though in annoyance. Nicola stared into the flames and wished she had the kind of sight Old Mairi had.

Angus handed her a glass. *"Slàinte!"* He touched the rim of his glass to hers.

"Cheers!" The silence, with him looking steadily at her, was unbearable. "Is it still snowing?" she asked at last.

"Steadily."

"That will be bad for the new lambs, won't it?"

"We rounded up quite a lot of the newborns today. They're in the barn. I'm hoping it'll only be a light fall."

"Is that what Jock says?" Nicola asked.

Angus swirled the mellow amber liquid around in his glass, watching the fire for a moment. "No, but Jock is a gloomy prophet at the best of times."

Nicola smiled slightly. "Maybe you should ask Mairi MacTavish."

He considered her for a moment. "Even she can be wrong."

Nicola raised an eyebrow. "Did she see things in your life that didn't happen?"

He swallowed his whisky and stared reflectively into the empty glass as though it might have the properties of a crystal ball. "Never before." He didn't explain and Nicola didn't press him, since she sensed he was referring to something intensely private.

"Life sometimes takes strange turns that even fortune-tellers can't predict, I suppose."

"Maybe."

Nicola was beginning to feel a little fuzzy from the alcohol and the warmth of the fire. "If you don't mind, Angus," she said at last, "I'll go up now. Thank you for the drink."

He reacted violently then. He snapped out of the reverie he'd sunk into and, grabbing her glass, slammed it down onto the mantelpiece with his hand. Before Nicola could move away his arms were restraining her. There was a long heart-stopping moment when he did nothing but look deeply into her eyes and then he kissed her, sweetly and tenderly, probing the depths of her emotions until she almost cried out. It was so blissful, yet so unbearable.

His lips lay lightly on her cheek, then traced the shape of her nose, nibbled at her ear and returned to explore the deep dimples close to her mouth. He whispered huskily, "Nicola, I love you and I want you, and we've got to do something about it."

"Such as breaking Rowena's heart? Even if there wasn't someone else, I wouldn't want to be responsible for that, Angus." She despised herself for the pious remark and insisted quickly, "I really think I'd better go to bed now."

He didn't try to prevent her and she glimpsed him turning to stare moodily into the fire again as she slipped quietly out the door.

Nicola woke next morning with the odd feeling that something was different. A peculiar stillness seemed to have settled on the room. It wasn't until she slid out of bed and drew the curtains back that she knew why. It was snowing.

Delicate flakes were pirouetting down like flower petals, dancing on the glass and drifting into a ridge of crystal along the windowsill. The world was white except for the dim grey shadows of outbuildings and the arching tree branches laden with snow.

The mountains were hidden, the loch invisible, too. Nicola gazed out, half entranced at the silent, pristine purity of the snow, until the cold coming through the glass made her draw the curtain back and retreat into the snug warmth of the room. She shivered and climbed into bed, staying there for another half hour before it was time to get up.

The first sign of Angus was when Nicola heard him kicking off his boots in the vestibule next to the kitchen. A few moments later he erupted into the room, clapping cold hands together, holding them out to the stove where she was stirring the porridge. There were flakes of snow melting in his dark hair and his cheeks and ears were rosy from cold and exertion.

"Jock wasn't wrong," Nicola said. Her voice sounded very flat to her. "It must have snowed all night."

Angus cupped his hands and blew into them. "It certainly did. I wish now we'd rounded up more of the lambs yesterday. It's drifting badly up on the hills, and the forecast, the official one that is, isn't optimistic." He glanced at her apologetically. "I'm afraid we might be snowed in for a day or two, or at worst a week."

Nicola concealed her dismay. "What are you going to do about the lambs?"

He sat down to his porridge. "Try to find as many as we can. There were probably a few dropped last night. They'd survive a light fall of snow, but they'll have a slim chance in deep drifts."

"How will you find them in deep snow?" Nicola asked anxiously, thinking of the tiny creatures so vulnerable in an icy wasteland.

"We know where the ewes will have sheltered—against stone walls, rocky outcrops, overhangs, fences and bushes. Some will have scraped out quite cosy little igloos and be warm as toast for a while, at any rate; but we'll have to prod the snow with long sticks until we locate others. We'll bring in as many animals as we can and take food to those we can't, if possible."

"It sounds a big job. What can I do to help?"

He grinned at her gratefully. "Thanks, but you'll be of more use here keeping the kettle on the boil and some soup on the hob. We might need bottles for some of the lambs, too. I'll let you know. And you can answer the phone. It was still on this morning when I got up, but I suspect the line might come down any minute. Meanwhile somebody might try to get through to us."

Like Magnus, Nicola thought at once. "Have any of your workers arrived today?" she asked.

He shook his head. "It's lucky Jock lives in the flat over the barn or I'd be stuck here on my own. I've rung the lads and told them to help whoever's nearest or whoever they can reach. Everyone's going to have his job cut out, seeing to stock."

A few minutes later he was gone.

"Take care," Nicola whispered as she looked through the kitchen window at his dark, hunched figure plunging through the deep snow in the yard.

CHAPTER EIGHT

SOME hours later he came back, carrying a tiny newborn lamb huddled under his coat. He grinned at Nicola as he put it into her arms. "See if you can keep this little fellow alive and kicking. He's a bit of a weakling."

"What shall I do with him?" she asked in alarm as she cradled the soft body close. "I don't know—"

"Give it a bottle and a warm box by the stove," Angus said abruptly.

When he'd gone again, Nicola fetched a cardboard box from the scullery and lined it with an old blanket she found there. She filled a bottle and after some initial difficulty, she managed to get the lamb to suckle. Presently, replete at last, it fell asleep on her lap, and then, when she finally could bring herself to move it, she put it in the box in front of the stove.

Later still, the back door slammed and an icy blast blew down the passageway, bringing Angus with it once more, this time to call her to the barn to give milk to several more lambs who, although they were still with their mothers, needed supplementary feeding.

Nicola prepared bottles, tucked them under her fleece-lined jacket and hurried out. Her feet sank deeply into the soft snow, but she didn't heed the wetness and in any case her shoes soon dried inside the barn, which was surprisingly warm despite its loftiness.

Rolf was standing sentinel at the door, but he made no objection to her entering and in fact gave her a friendly nudge. From within came an intermittent chorus of bleats from the crowd of ewes and their lambs now sheltering there. Angus was helping Jock to load bales of fodder onto the sledge which had brought most of the sheep to safety, so that those still out on the hillsides would have food to keep them going through the spell of unexpected wintry weather.

"They're a hardy breed," Angus told Nicola. "Once they're fully grown, I've known them to survive a week or more in a snowdrift so long as they had air and a few tussocks of grass." He laughed. "Snow is warm and so is wool."

Nicola shivered despite the heat in the barn. Snow didn't seem a warm commodity at the moment. Presently, her task with the lambs complete, she dashed back to the house to serve up a hot lunch to the two men.

Jock usually fended for himself, but today was different. He came in with Angus and when the two men trudged across the yard from the barn, Nicola was at the kitchen door scattering crumbs for the birds. Some sparrows and a blackbird were competing eagerly for the food, and a cheeky robin was hopping close to her feet, eyeing her saucily.

"That's the idea," Angus said approvingly, and Nicola caught a look in his eyes that made her heart turn over.

She glanced at the sky. It had stopped snowing and the ceiling of clouds had lifted a little. "It's stopped," she said unnecessarily, because she felt ill at ease in his presence.

"For the moment," said Angus grimly. "Jock reckons there's more to come. So does the weather bureau."

Both were proved right. As night fell it began to snow again. Nicola's work for the day didn't finish with the onset of darkness. She was still needed to ferry more bottles across to the barn for the hungry lambs. The exertions of the day eventually caught up with her and she faltered once or twice in the deep snow. She had scarcely paused all day between tending her charges in the kitchen—now increased to three—providing food for the men and helping distribute fodder to the animals in the barn.

When Angus and Jock came in for their evening meal, late, they both looked weary, but each put away a hearty dinner and seemed satisfied with the day's work.

"We couldna've done any more," Jock commented. "I reckon we got most of the lambs in—excepting some that might be higher up."

"Aye," agreed Angus, passing a hand wearily across his forehead.

Nicola met his eyes and turned away quickly because of the wrench in her heart—the heart that somehow couldn't harden against him, much as she might wish it.

"We'll try and get to them tomorrow," Angus continued.

After Jock had retired to his quarters over the barn, Angus said, "He reckons we can expect a thaw pretty soon, maybe the day after tomorrow."

She pulled a face. "He can be that precise? How long will it take for the roads to be cleared?"

"Depends on how many snowploughs are on the job, how bad it is elsewhere. By the way, have you tried the phone recently?"

Nicola shook her head. "I had no reason to make any calls, but I'm sure it hasn't rung. I've been within earshot most of the time. I suppose it might be out of order."

Angus yawned. "I'll check."

He returned to tell her the phone was off. "The line must have come down with that last snowstorm, so now we're well and truly marooned."

"Does it happen often in winter? Craigmoor House is very isolated."

"Not as often as you might think." He gave her a lazy grin. "Scared?"

"Scared? Why should I be scared?"

"Being cut off. Stuck here all alone with me."

"Really, Angus," she said. "That isn't even funny."

He raked his hair wearily. "No. Lousy joke. Sorry. Must be tired."

He looked all in and Nicola felt a wave of compassion. "You must get some rest," she said. "You'll collapse if you don't take a break." She paused. "Is there anything I can get you? A whisky?"

He slumped into a chair. "A large cup of very strong, sweet tea would be wonderful. I'll take a shower while you're making it. And then it's bed for both of us. You've worked as hard as anyone today, Nicola." He rose stiffly as though all his joints were protesting, and placed a hand on her shoulder, leaning towards her slightly. "Thanks, Nicola. You've done a sterling job." Then, hastily, as though it pained him to have to say it, he added, "I'm sorry if it seemed I was harassing you. You're right, of course. I won't embarrass you by saying another word about us. It's quite impossible. I was just . . . a little mad for a moment."

Nicola's throat was so tightly constricted, she could scarcely swallow, let alone speak. But Angus evidently didn't require an answer. In a flash he was gone. Briefly she let the rush of emotion he had stirred overwhelm her and then angrily blinked the tears away and put the kettle on.

She heard the plumbing complain as Angus took his shower, then there was silence. Some minutes passed and he didn't reappear. Guessing what had happened, Nicola tiptoed upstairs and along the landing to his room. The door was slightly ajar, and she made no sound as she pushed it open and looked in. Angus was spread-eagled on the bed in his dressing gown, a crumpled damp towel on the nearby chair. He was dead to the world.

Nicola wasn't afraid of waking him. Nothing would make him stir until morning, she felt certain. Nevertheless she moved quietly, and with care not to make any sudden noise that would rouse him. She folded the free half of the coverlet he was lying on over him, spread out his towel on the radiator in the bathroom, and then stood for a moment looking down at the sleeping man. He had already regretted his temporary infatuation, as she'd felt sure he would, but she still loved him. He would always be a part of her now.

She ran swiftly downstairs again and grimaced at the pot of strong tea. She poured some into her own cup, adding hot water to weaken it. She was about to tip the remainder down the sink when, on impulse, she fetched a vacuum flask and filled it. She placed it with a cup and saucer and a covered dish of oatmeal biscuits on a tray, and once again tiptoed upstairs and into Angus's room. He was still deeply asleep, but if he did wake later on, he might appreciate the tea, she thought. The tray made a slight sound as she placed it on the bedside table, but he didn't stir an eyelash. Nicola drew in a long, slow breath, feasting her eyes on the calm, relaxed features on the pillow, and another idea came to her. She dashed downstairs and swiftly returned with the bottle of whisky and a glass, which she also placed on the tray, smiling to herself. If he didn't wake before morning, at least he could have an early breakfast—of a sort.

Reluctantly she left the bedroom and went back to the kitchen. Her own weariness seemed to have abated and she felt wide-awake. More because she wanted something to occupy her than because it was necessary, she made up some bottles for the lambs. Those in the kitchen were contentedly huddled together and apparently not hungry, so she flung on her coat and ran across the yard to the barn to see if any of the newborns there needed sustenance.

The snow was crisp underfoot now, the sky black and high and the air crisp and frosty. Jock had shovelled a path from the house to the barn to make the going easier. The light fall of snow covering the cleared way wasn't deep, but was a little slippery, and Nicola skidded once or twice.

Jock wasn't in the barn, and Nicola made her way amongst the lambs looking for any that seemed hungry. She fed two tiny ones under the watchful eyes of their mothers, and then sat down wearily for a moment on a bale of hay. She felt unable to rouse herself to go back to the house. Exhaustion claimed her suddenly, and it was some time later when she jerked awake to feel warm fingers gently massaging the back of her neck and loosening her shoulder muscles. She turned round and her heart skipped a beat.

"Angus, I thought you were asleep."

"I was. Out like a light," he said without ceasing his ministrations. "But I woke up to find somebody had been thoughtful enough to bring me tea in a thermos, and the bottle of Scotch." His fingers strayed briefly into her hair, making her scalp tingle. In a low murmur he added, "Looking after people and animals seems to be your forte." There was a smile in his voice, and Nicola, her lids still heavy and threatening to close, longed to lean back in his arms and sleep there.

"I must have dozed off," she muttered.

"You've been here for hours. Come on, let's get you to bed." He stood up, taking her hand and drawing her onto her feet. Nicola swayed as sleep tried to claim her. She tried valiantly to shake it off, but failed. Angus caught her deftly in his arms, lifted her up and carried her back to the house.

Nicola came to briefly, realising she was lying on her bed and that someone was tucking her in. Her eyelids flickered and she saw dimly that it was Angus. His lips brushed hers in a fleeting caress and warm fingertips gently pushed strands of hair from her forehead and made the pillow more comfortable under her head. Then the bedside lamp was switched off and she was in darkness. She heard only a quiet click as her door closed behind him, and she descended into oblivion once more.

When she woke the room was still dark, but her alarm clock told her it was morning. It took a minute or two for her brain to begin functioning clearly and her body to rise from the torpor of deep sleep.

The first thing she realised was that she was in her nightgown. She had a vague recollection now of stepping out of her jeans, and of her sweater being pulled over her head. She didn't remember it, but he must have helped her undress. She remembered him tucking her in, though, and the blissful feeling she had enjoyed as he had kissed her good-night.

Nicola languished for a few minutes, clinging to the warmth of the bed before she roused herself and got up. She went straight to the window. Dawn was just breaking and she felt sure that it hadn't snowed again in the night. The world was still white, but the cloud cover was high in the lightening sky and she could faintly see the forbidding hulks of the mountains. Perhaps they would have no more snow. She fervently hoped so. If she could have vanished then and there, like ice melting into the ground, she gladly would have done so, but she would have to be patient and wait until the roads were clear enough for driving.

And then what? She hadn't even begun to think about her future. Only one thing was clear: she would write no more features for *Private Lives*, and Hugh Vanter would have no part of her life, even as her boss. What she would do, she hadn't the faintest idea.

I wish I had the sight, like Old Mairi, she thought. The old woman had said that everyone had it if they bothered to use it, and maybe she was right, but that morning Nicola could see nothing in the future but the bleakness of living without Angus.

In spite of his interrupted night, Angus had evidently gotten up early and he came in as usual for breakfast, looking slightly harassed.

He warmed his hands on the teapot. "Jock and I will be out on the hills all morning, so could you make us a couple of flasks of coffee and some sandwiches? I doubt if we'll be finished by lunchtime. We need to check some of the higher slopes we couldn't reach yesterday."

Nicola nodded. "I'll do it straightaway."

"Have your breakfast first, lass," Angus murmured, giving her a warm, approving smile. "There's no great rush. I shan't be dashing off till I've had mine."

Nicola would have preferred busying herself cutting sandwiches to sitting opposite Angus at the table, feeling acutely aware of him, but she did as he said. She hurried through her breakfast so as not to keep him waiting when he'd finished his.

"We'll leave you to keep an eye on the lambs in the barn," Angus said, zipping up his windproof jacket and clamping a thick woollen hat down over his ears. He slung the backpack she had prepared over his shoulders. "Keep warm and don't exhaust yourself."

"And you take care," she murmured. "It'll be treacherous up there."

He paused, looking steadily at her with a slightly wistful smile on his lips, and impulsively lifted a hand and rumpled her hair. "Don't worry. I'm as surefooted as a stag in high places, and so is Jock."

After they'd gone, Nicola found plenty to occupy her and the time flew faster than she'd expected. It was late afternoon and Angus and Jock hadn't yet returned, when a familiar sound in the distance broke the silence. Nicola rushed outside and saw, barely a quarter of a mile away, the sun glinting on a great wave of snow that was being thrust into the air by a plough.

She raced back to the kitchen to put the kettle on, feeling sure the plough operators would welcome a hot drink and something to eat, and was glad she'd spent part of the morning baking bread and fruit buns. As a result she didn't notice the car which had been travelling a short distance behind the plough.

She heard the engine of the plough finally cut and was about to dash out to offer refreshment to the crew, when a cold draught of air sliced down the passageway as the back door was opened. A large red-haired man sauntered into the kitchen.

He looked surprised. "Hello! Where's Morag? I thought she was going to fill in for Binnie." He looked Nicola over quizzically. "Should I know you?"

"No. I'm—well, it's a long story. But I'm here instead of Morag who's been down with the flu. My name's Nicola Sharman. I heard the snowplough and I was just coming to ask if you'd like tea or coffee and something to eat," Nicola said. "Is there just you, or—?"

He laughed heartily. "I'm not part of the crew, Miss Sharman. But I'm sure the two lads will appreciate a hot drink and something to eat. I told them to come in. I was driving behind. I've been trying to get home for two days, but the dratted snow held me up."

"Home!" Nicola stared at him, realisation dawning. She'd just made another gaffe. This must be Lord Kilgarrin, and she'd mistaken him for a snowplough operator.

But he upset this idea by saying, "Where's Magnus?"

"He's not here, I'm afraid. But who—?"

He held out his hand. "Sorry. Angus Macpherson. Lord Kilgarrin's estate manager. Glad to meet you, Miss Sharman. What a time for me to choose to be away. I made it back to Glasgow and then got caught on the way up."

Nicola gaped at him openmouthed for an incredible, mind-boggling moment while her brain screamed *It can't be!* "Did you say Angus Macpherson?" she asked numbly, silently begging him to deny it and negate the terrible truth that was suddenly dawning on her.

He looked at her curiously. "That's right, lassie." He laughed. "Finding Scottish accents a little hard to follow, are you? You're Australian, by the sound of yours."

"Yes."

"Well, I won't ask how you come to be housekeeping for Magnus, not right now. I'd better get along and lend a hand. I suppose Magnus and Jock have been having a rough time. Where are they, out on the hills searching for casualties?"

Nicola couldn't stop staring at him. "Yes," she answered vaguely, and then collected her wits. "They've been out since early morning. I daresay they'll be back soon."

"I think I can guess where they're most likely to be. I'll just go down to The Rowans and change and get after them." He turned back at the door. "You don't happen to know if Rowena's back from Inverness, I suppose, and if anything's happened about the renovations at the house?"

His question fazed Nicola for a moment, then she remembered. "Yes, I think it's all been sorted out. Rowena telephoned before the snow."

He chuckled. "Trust Rowena! I knew she'd stand for no nonsense." He added, "Have you met her?"

"No, we've only spoken on the telephone."

"Terrific girl. I'm lucky. I wish the phones weren't out, though. I only got back from overseas yesterday, and I couldn't get through to her from the airport," he grumbled. "This phone's out, too. I tried to get through to you last night."

"Yes, the line's been down since the second big snowstorm."

"Well, first things first," he said, and grinned. "I'd better get cracking. See you later."

There was a clatter in the passage and two young men came into the kitchen as Angus went out. For the next few minutes, Nicola was too busy providing food and drink for the snowplough crew to allow her mind to dwell on the shattering discovery that the man she'd believed was Angus Macpherson must be Magnus Lord. *Magnus Lord. Lord Kilgarrin.* And he'd fooled her as successfully as she had fooled him. More so, in fact, since he had been suspicious of her, but not once had she dreamed that he was not who he said he was.

When the two men had left, Nicola cleared up and let herself think at last. Waves of anger and humiliation alternated as her mind reviewed the events of the past few days. How he must have been laughing at her! He had even persuaded others to help him in his deception. Mrs. Ross, Jock, Archie McClintoch, Rowena, Lady Catriona and her father, even Old Mairi.

She'd put the idea in his head herself, of course, by mistaking him for a gamekeeper, and he'd found a simple and ironic way to punish her. He knew she would never recognise him. The few published pictures of him had been when he was clean-shaven and fifteen years younger, and even in those his features had never been perfectly clear.

At first he must have gone along with her mistake because he'd suspected she was a journalist, and was trying to put her off the scent. But later he'd trusted her and invited her to stay on, so why hadn't he confessed then? It couldn't have been easy for him to maintain the pretence, as it hadn't been for her to deceive him. Now she thought about it, there had been small clues, of course, but she'd been too preoccupied with maintaining her own deception to be suspicious of him.

His proprietorial air had puzzled her, but she'd easily explained it away. He'd moved from his own bedroom to fool her into thinking he was living in the house only temporarily, and even his silk pyjamas and expensive dressing gown hadn't made her wonder. Lady Catriona had said he was rich and, knowing nothing about him, Nicola had accepted her words without thinking. And there was Rolf. She should have realised that the old saying, "No dog can have two masters," was true. Rolf was indubitably Angus's—no, Magnus's dog.

But she should have been suspicious, Nicola thought, angry with herself for her lack of perception, when he showed such violent antipathy towards the Press. His vehemence had been too strong, even for a loyal friend. But she'd let her imagination hide the truth from her. She'd believed he'd been in love with Jacynth himself—which he had been, of course.

"Oh, God," she moaned. "What an idiot I've been."

It was no wonder Catriona had been jealous! And no wonder Rowena hadn't seemed at all perturbed that she was alone with her fiancé—because she hadn't been. She had been alone with Magnus Lord.

Thoughts crowded in on Nicola as she sat brooding at the kitchen table. Now that the first shock of discovery was abating, she realised that everything that had happened had acquired a totally new perspective. And the most difficult area she had to reassess was that the man she had believed to be Angus Macpherson was not engaged to marry Rowena McAllister.

For a few moments this realisation made her heart race unnaturally. "But why didn't he tell me that?" Nicola wondered aloud, and then silently answered herself. Because she had told him she was going to marry Hugh, that she wouldn't cancel her wedding for him. She could hardly blame him for continuing the deception, for preferring that she never knew who he really was.

But supposing she told him now that she had lied about Hugh in self-defence? What then? Was Angus—Magnus—really in love with her? Nicola shook her head sadly. Even if he was now, it would be a different story when she confessed who she really was. Did she really imagine that Lord Kilgarrin would consider marrying her, a reporter on a third-rate—as she now thought of it—magazine, who had masqueraded as a bird-watcher in order to probe his private suffering; who had lied about her father, exaggerated her social position and pretended her fiancé was a tycoon? Nicola shuddered at the thought. Whatever had possessed her to let Hugh Vanter talk her into this crazy escapade? The sooner she extricated herself, the better. And the sooner she wrote and posted her letter of resignation to Hugh, also the better.

It was nearly dusk, and the men would be returning soon. Nicola didn't pause to consider whether she would have time. She simply fled upstairs and flung her few possessions into her suitcase and within minutes was downstairs and heading for the garage where her car was parked. There was no time to leave a note, but Angus—Magnus—would know why she had gone.

Let him explain to the real Angus, she thought, half angrily, tears stinging her eyes as she got into her car and turned on the ignition. The engine was cold and it was a minute or two before it started. Nicola was trembling with anxiety as she backed out of the garage and into the yard.

"Don't let them come back yet," she begged Providence. "Let me get away."

She almost did. She got as far as the gate and saw the back road stretched out tantalisingly before her, a dark ribbon between ridges of snow. But as she got back into the car after opening the gate, a figure emerged from the nearest copse, ahead of her almost directly in her path. It was Magnus Lord.

He looked astonished to see her driving away, and since she could hardly run him down, she had to wait until he came up to her. His cold-pinched face filled her side window.

"What's this? Where are you going?"

She made a helpless gesture with her hands. "Just going. Leaving."

"Now? It's nearly dark. You can't drive across the moor in the dark."

"The road's been cleared."

"There could be slides. There are huge drifts beside the road. You could get stranded. Why, Nicola? I know you're anxious to get away, but why so precipitately?"

"Haven't you seen Angus?" Nicola asked, enunciating the words slowly, in a dry tone.

Instantly his face changed and became a battleground of conflicting emotions. "No." His voice was hollow. "He's back?"

"Yes. He went to find you and Jock. I thought you'd have met up, and in the circumstances you understand, I'm sure, why I'd want to leave at once."

"I went to see if Old Mairi was all right," he said, and then, "Wait, Nicola. I want to talk to you." The knuckles of his bare hand gripping the car windowsill were white with tension.

He raced around the car and jumped into the passenger seat, half turning to face her. "I'm sorry. It was a despicable thing to do to you."

"You don't have to apologise. I'm just not sure I fully understand why you kept it up after—"

"After I decided you weren't a wicked spy from the gutter Press? Nicola, it was just a joke at first. When you mistook me for a gamekeeper, I couldn't resist letting you go on thinking I was one. I thought it was an easy way to get rid of you and stop you pestering me. It was very satisfying to dupe a member of the Press, as I first thought you must be. I thought your twisting your ankle was a fake so I took you on a long, tiring walk to punish you. Then I realised I was probably being as paranoid as you insisted I was, and that I was taking out my venom on a perfectly innocent party. A woman so delightful—"

"Why didn't you tell me who you really were when you invited me to stay? Did you have to involve everyone else in your little game?"

He smiled ruefully. "It was madness, but how else could I keep the truth from you, even in those first few hours? It's extraordinary how things get out of hand when you start deceiving someone." The smile broadened. "Scott knew what he was talking about when he wrote 'Oh, what a tangled web we weave,/ When first we practise to deceive!'"

"Didn't he also say, 'The best laid plans o' mice and men/ Gang oft astray'?"

"No, that's Robbie Burns. In fact he said, 'The best laid schemes o' mice and men/ Gang aft a-gley.'"

His hand seemed to reach out of its own accord to touch her face. "I certainly didn't plan to fall in love with you."

"Don't talk like that, Ang—Mag—Lord Kilgarrin," Nicola faltered.

"My name is Magnus. Please call me that. If you hadn't told me about this man in Sydney, Australia, that you're determined to marry, Nicola, I would have confessed long ago," Magnus said. "I was trying to on several occasions. That day on the island, Nicola, I was sure you'd guess, but you didn't. You said you believed me innocent; you said you trusted Angus, the man I was pretending to be. How could I tell you I wasn't as honest as you supposed? I felt you were falling in love with me as I was with you, but you were falling for the wrong person—the person I was pretending to be. It was all so complicated. And there was the past, hanging over me as it has for fifteen years, making it all so much more complicated—impossible, I thought.''

"I don't think we should try to analyse it," Nicola said slowly. "I think we'll only make matters worse. I'd like to go, Ang—Magnus. Please get out and let me go.''

He placed a restraining hand on the steering wheel, shaking his head. "No. It's too risky. Don't be foolish, Nicola. You've no need to feel humiliated. The real Angus will think it's a huge joke, and if you don't tell them to punish me, no one will know I made a fool of myself over you.''

"I'm the one who looks a fool. Everybody knows how easily you duped me. They're all laughing fit to burst, I don't doubt.'' She had no right to feel so outraged, she thought ruefully—not when she had perpetrated as bad or even worse a deception herself. But she hadn't been found out.

He looked steadily at her. "No, they aren't. Everyone's sympathies will be with you. They all thought I was mad—Binnie, Jock, Archie, even Catriona, although her sense of humour is a bit warped. Back up through the gate, please, Nicola. At least stay until tomorrow. I won't stop you going then. I daresay Morag will arrive early on to relieve you, anyway. But I'd never forgive myself if anything happened to you on the road tonight.''

The long, cold shadows across the snow sent a chilly shiver through Nicola. It would be horrible to be stranded on the moor. Maybe if she just treated the whole thing as humorous and attempted to show that she took it in good part, she could get through the evening. Now that Angus was back, Magnus and he would have a lot to talk about and wouldn't bother her. Perhaps she had been a bit precipitate, leaving at this late hour.

"All right," she said reluctantly and shifted the gears into reverse. She felt Magnus relax in the seat beside her. Magnus! she thought, still incredulous. Lord Kilgarrin. Magnus Lord wasn't a shadowy figure in the back of her mind anymore; he was flesh and blood—and sitting beside her. She'd been living with him for a week.

As they walked into the house together, Magnus said cheerfully, "You had me worried there for a minute, Nicola. I thought I was going to have to get dinner myself."

"I guessed that was the real reason you wanted me back. My safety was merely a secondary consideration," she teased, matching his lightness, seeking to establish a tone for their last few hours together.

But he clearly took her seriously. He stopped and caught her by the shoulders firmly. "Nicola, your safety would always concern me above everything else."

"It's cold out here," Nicola said, letting her teeth chatter to prove it, and shrugging off his grasp while longing for the warmth of his arms about her. "Let's go in."

The real Angus Macpherson thought the whole masquerade was an enormous joke and sympathised with Nicola exclusively, as Magnus had said he would.

"I wonder you're still speaking to him," Angus declared. "It shows what a forgiving person you are. I can imagine how he would have reacted if you'd been deceiving him and you'd kept it up for days. He would have been livid and would never have forgiven you. Especially if you'd really been a journalist. Magnus despises all reporters, and I guess by now he's told you why." He glanced at his employer expectantly.

"Yes, I've told her," Magnus said shortly.

"It was a rotten business," Angus went on. "Nobody likes to be judged unfairly. But that's all in the past now."

Nicola's eyes met Magnus's and she knew it wasn't all in the past. The bitterness was still there, etched into his soul. She also saw a desperate plea in his face that she would never repeat the confidences she had heard from him. She tried to reassure him without actually saying so.

After dinner the three of them had coffee in the sitting room, then Angus, having discovered that the phones were working, excused himself, saying he would go back to The Rowans and call Rowena. As she said good-night to him, Nicola felt absolutely sure that he had never been in love with Jacynth. He would have only been a boy of fourteen or fifteen then, anyway, she realised. Angus was years younger than Magnus and probably hadn't even been living on the estate then.

Magnus lingered at the door chatting with Angus for a few minutes, and then looked into the kitchen where Nicola was clearing up, saying, "I've got a few things to attend to. I expect you'd like an early night." He was doing his best, she thought gratefully, to save her embarrassment.

"Yes. I'll go up as soon as I'm done here."

But Nicola didn't go upstairs when she had finished. She sat at the kitchen table drinking the reheated dregs of coffee and thinking about Old Mairi and what she'd said on the road that first day: *Never to return*. In her vision, she had seen a woman leaving the house, and she'd agreed that the woman was Nicola. It was going to come true. Nicola had tried to leave today and Magnus had brought her back, but there was nothing to stop her from going tomorrow and returning to Sydney as soon as she could get a booking on an aircraft. Unless... Suddenly she was also remembering the old woman's words about people having the sight, but not using it.

Her pulse ran raggedly as she imagined the alternative. The future was the result of what happened in the present, Old Mairi had said. The future depended on what you did with the present. If Magnus hadn't stopped her going tonight... Was it somehow prophetic that he had? Had she been given an opportunity to use her sight? Nicola moistened her lips nervously because all her thoughts were leading her to the one thing she had avoided all along: confession. She had given herself a hundred excuses for not revealing the truth, but the prime one was cowardice; not wanting Magnus to despise her.

Now, all at once, she told herself that she had nothing to lose. If Magnus loved her, he would forgive her, as she had forgiven him. But in spite of what he'd said, she wasn't sure that he did love her. Maybe it had been a brief madness on his part. He wasn't going to marry Rowena, to be sure, but there was still Lady Catriona; and he had been somewhat reticent about her.

Nicola contemplated her ringless hands and reminded herself that he was also Lord Kilgarrin, and therefore much more likely to marry into another aristocratic Scottish clan than to wed the daughter of a modest Australian motel-keeper, a woman who had once belonged to the profession he despised. It would be a double shock to him to find out that her father wasn't the rich entrepreneur that Magnus had assumed he was. But if he loved her, would anything else matter?

Again and again the phrase hammered in her brain, until she knew she would never have any peace unless she found out for certain. If she went back to Australia, Magnus Lord would haunt her and she would always wonder, if she had only had the courage to tell him the truth, the courage to gamble on the future she knew would bring happiness, would things have turned out differently?

Slowly her thoughts crystallised into resolution. Logically she reduced her complex feelings to a simple formula. If Magnus's love turned to loathing at her revelation, all that would happen was that he would rail at her, and she would still leave as planned in the morning. If she left without telling him, at least his image of her would remain untarnished, but she would never know if he had really *loved her*. And if he did love her, then, through her cowardice, she would have lost the only man she would ever feel for as deeply as she did for him. Always it came back to that—until her uncertainties were crushed beneath the weight of needing to know the truth.

Nicola glanced at the clock on the kitchen wall. It wasn't late and Magnus was probably still working in the study. He would likely appreciate a cup of tea, and taking one to him would give her the opportunity she wanted. She was trembling nervously as she boiled the water and at the study door she almost lost her nerve altogether. Even when she finally did knock and he called out "Come in," she wasn't sure she could go through with it. She stood inside the room, transfixed for a moment by the image of him seated behind his desk, looking slightly surprised to see her.

"Is that tea?" he asked. "That was a kind thought, Nicola."

"I thought you might like a cup," she said. "I decided to have one myself before I went to bed."

"There's only one cup," he observed. "Why don't you go and get yours?"

"No, it's all right," she said, faltering, knowing that if she was going to tell him it had to be now. "I—I also wanted a word with you...."

"All the more reason to fetch your tea," he insisted.

Nicola shook her head. "No, it won't take long. There's something I have to tell you."

Instantly he was alert, leaning forward eagerly. "Nicola? Have you—is it about this man you think you want to marry? For God's sake tell me it is." He rose and came close to where she was standing, his grey eyes searching her face eagerly. "Tell me you've changed your mind."

Nicola stepped back a pace. "Yes, it is about him, partly. But, Ang—Magnus, things are much more complicated than you think."

His eyes narrowed a fraction and he folded his arms across his chest. His expression now, Nicola thought, almost suggested that he had a sixth sense about what was to come. The suspicion that had lurked in those penetrating grey eyes in the beginning was surely there again now.

"Well?" he asked expectantly.

Nicola took a deep breath. There was no retreating now.

CHAPTER NINE

For a very long moment there was no sound in the room from the two people in it. The silence was so intense, the atmosphere so highly charged that Nicola was acutely aware of the crackling of the fire Magnus had lit and of the erratic beating of her heart.

She was aware, too, that she had travelled beyond the point of no return and that whether she lived to regret it or not, she must now say what she had come to say.

"Well, Nicola?" Magnus Lord seemed to tower over her and was, as he had been on their first encounter, very intimidating. She was suddenly aware of Rolf, too, sprawled near the fire but observing her with a half-open eye. Even he looked suspicious of her, she thought.

"I have a confession to make," Nicola said quickly. "I—I felt I should before I left—"

"'Confession'?" The word hovered ominously between them.

Nicola looked at the carpet and knew she would never be able to forget its pattern. She must get this over quickly. It was tearing her apart to delay, and yet the words were so difficult to say.

"Ang—Magnus . . ." His real name still sounded awkward on her tongue. "I'm afraid you guessed right the first time. I am a journalist and I did come here with the intention of getting the inside story on why Magnus Lord gave up filmmaking and what he's doing now. I work—worked—for a magazine called *Private Lives* and we've been running a very successful series on 'Whatever happened to' a number of personalities who dropped out of sight during the past few years. When the managing editor of the magazine group heard that local television was planning a festival of Jacynth Moore's best films—''

She got no further. Magnus broke in incredulously, ''Am I mad, or are you really telling me that I was right all the time, that you're just a sneaky little reporter after a story, that all the rest was a fake?'' His voice began to shake.

''I'm sorry, Magnus. I understand how you feel, and—''

His eyes were chips of steel-grey ice. ''I doubt you do, Nicola. I can't believe it. You! A fake. No, I refuse to believe it.'' But the storm gathering in those eyes that had sometimes looked at her so tenderly, sometimes so passionately, showed that he was beginning to.

''I'm afraid it's true. And I'm afraid everything I told you about myself and my family is a fiction. Well, most of it. My father is in the hotel business, but he isn't the wealthy entrepreneur I pretended he was. He owns a small motel on the north coast of New South Wales. The man I told you I was going to marry is the managing editor of the group of magazines to which *Private Lives* belongs.''

Magnus felt stunned. She had fooled him and taken him for an idiot, using all her wiles to get a story out of him even though she didn't know he was Magnus Lord. And he'd played right into her hands, telling her things he'd never told his friends, much less a reporter. It hurt, it really hurt, that she had deceived him so glibly, that all her warmth and passion were pretence, for effect, calculated to trick and beguile him. Her goal all along had been to get him to tell her enough about Magnus Lord so that it wouldn't matter if she never met her real subject. Nothing mattered to her except getting a good story. Just like all those other journalists fifteen years ago who hadn't regarded the suffering of another human being, so long as they could file a story.

Nicola watched his eyes fill with fury and contempt and his features set hard as granite. But he didn't raise his voice. "Well, you got your story," he said in a curiously flat, tired tone. "I daresay you got some photographs, too, when I wasn't looking. I'm sure your article will make interesting reading."

"Magnus, I don't intend to write anything about you," Nicola said slowly. "Since you talked to me not knowing who I really was, that wouldn't be ethical."

Magnus's calm was disintegrating. Such a tumult of emotions was erupting inside him, he hardly knew which was what. At last, the only way he could cope with what she had told him, his only refuge from the wounds she was inflicting, was anger.

"Ethical!" he thundered. "There's nothing ethical about you, Nicola Sharman. There never has been about your kind. I wouldn't believe a word you said about anything, now. You wouldn't keep promises. I just hope you get some satisfaction out of what you're doing, because I'm damn sure nobody else will, except perhaps those ghoulish readers of your trashy magazine!"

"*Private Lives* is not trashy," Nicola said stoutly. "And all my articles so far have been thoroughly researched and approved by their subjects. I know you would never approve anything I wrote, so I won't be writing anything about you." Making a superhuman effort, she looked him straight in the eye. "I have some integrity, Magnus."

He looked unconvinced. "Integrity? You really expect me to believe that you went to all this trouble just to end up shelving the story? Why, Nicola? It's a good story. Not just an interview, but firsthand experience."

There was so much derision in his tone, she couldn't say she wasn't filing the story because she loved him. He wouldn't believe that. She was a fool to have confessed. She had gained nothing by it, and she had only diminished herself in Magnus's eyes. Nicola knew she had gambled and lost. Magnus didn't love her enough to forgive her. He'd been deceived too often by Jacynth Moore and pilloried too mercilessly by the Press. She was a reminder of those two shattering experiences. How could she have expected him to forgive? That was too much for any man.

A burst of faintly ironic laughter escaped him. "Is this how you get all your stories? By masquerading as a bird-watcher?" His tone was scathing, and Nicola flinched.

"No! That was only because I discovered your interest in ornithology. Anyway, most of my subjects have been cooperative, even flattered to be rediscovered. Only a few have refused to be interviewed. As I—I'd had some success persuading an ex-politician to let me interview him, Hugh suggested I try a similar approach with you."

"What did you masquerade as for the politician?" Magnus enquired, with a derisive twist to his mouth.

"A sheepshearers' cook," she admitted reluctantly.

Although every second was twisting the knife deeper, Magnus laughed in spite of himself. "Well, you get marks for enterprise, I grant you that. Who's your next victim?"

"There won't be any. I'm quitting."

He didn't accept that any more than anything else she'd said. "Don't bother to soft-soap me, Nicola. You're no doubt as adept at pretending remorse and reform as you are at everything else. The minute you're back in Sydney, lover boy will persuade you to write the Magnus Lord story, and next week you'll be off on another assignment—that is, if you have time, what with wedding preparations—"

"I'm not getting married," Nicola burst out. "That was all part of the deception. Hugh's nothing to me."

Her voice rose shrilly because she knew he didn't believe her.

Magnus regarded her stonily. With chill finality, he said, "And you're nothing to me now, Nicola. Don't think you can go on conning me. I'm not that much of a pushover. And I'm not so naïve that I don't know that to some people, Lord Kilgarrin is a much better catch than his estate manager. Is that why you came back so readily yesterday? Is that what this sudden change of heart is really all about? Are you going to pretend to be in love with me next?"

Nicola staggered as though she'd been struck. "That's a despicable thing to say! You don't really think I'm making excuses because..." But she saw that he did. It was so awful, she was rendered speechless.

Magnus said grittily, "Go home and marry your 'tycoon.' Who knows, with the kinds of ideas he dreams up, and your expertise in carrying them out, he might even become one. And get a knighthood for it. I'm sure you deserve each other, anyway."

Nicola wanted to yell at him that the only reason she had confessed was because she did love him; but she knew he wouldn't believe her now. Magnus's hatred of the Press was deep and abiding, and she had done nothing to mitigate it. She had simply stirred up all his old antipathy and directed it against herself. And his reaction meant that what he felt for her was easily erased and she had been a fool to imagine for a moment that it might be otherwise.

Magnus's anger and disappointment, his deep hurt, frustration and chagrin mingled to bring him close to the breaking point. To see her standing there telling him how she had deceived him was like being lashed to a stake and set on fire. He was sure that she must have an ulterior motive for speaking out now. Why hadn't she confessed before? Because there had been no advantage in doing so.

And now, it seemed, having discovered who he really was and how he felt about her, she had suddenly realised that there might be. She had believed she could wrap him around her little finger, that he would readily forgive her. But she was wrong. He was not so much a fool as to be taken in again.

"I wish I'd thrown you out that first night," he said through gritted teeth, "mist or no mist. It would have served you right if you had lost your way."

"You can throw me out now if you want."

He regarded her derisively. "I'm not a bully and I wouldn't want to feel responsible if you had an accident on an icy road. You can stay till morning, Miss Sharman, but I want you off the estate as soon as possible. I want you out of my sight before I do cease to be responsible for my actions. And when you're writing your colourful personal-experience story, just remember that I might always change my mind about suing if your magazine prints one word that is libellous."

"I told you, Magnus, there will be no story. I promise—"

"I don't believe you. How could I possibly believe anything you said now? I can't stop you using the information you gained from me, but I warn you, if you try to ruin Jacynth's reputation by your revelations, even fifteen years after her death, I'll take you through every court in your country and some in the British Isles as well. Jacynth was a very fine actress; she might have been a great one had she lived and conquered her own particular, private hell. But her personal life is none of your or your readers' business. If it suits you to muckrake, watch out. You might get a little publicity for yourself that neither you nor your precious managing-editor fiancé will welcome."

"Are you threatening me?" Nicola tilted her chin up, but her lips were trembling.

Magnus glimpsed the dismay in her face and tried to ignore it. "Yes," he said. She had never looked more beautiful, he thought. He felt so torn between fury and loving, he wondered if he would survive.

"You've no need," Nicola said. "I told you I wouldn't write anything, and I meant it."

"I don't care what you do," he said, feigning indifference. "You can't hurt me, but Jacynth isn't here to defend herself."

"You still love her, don't you?" Nicola whispered, and knew she was beaten, not by Magnus's fury, but by the ghost of a once-famous actress to whom, in spite of what he had told her about his marriage, he was still intensely loyal.

Magnus didn't answer. It was a question he had been asking himself often during the past few days. And the answer—the one he had given her on the island, the answer he had never really faced up to before—had been disturbing at first, then acceptable. For too long he had sought refuge in false memories and the bitterness of the past, calling it love, but it hadn't been. It had taken a woman from the other side of the world who tumbled into his life and turned it upside down, to make him realise that he was capable of loving someone else. Someone fresh and young and uncomplicated, someone honest and candid and not devious as Jacynth had been, and someone, he had flattered himself briefly, who was in love with him, too. It had happened so unexpectedly, he had doubted his own riotous feelings at first. But not for long. Nicola had swiftly conquered every question in his mind.

But now to discover that she was a fake, that it was all a fiction, and that she was as calculating as Jacynth had ever been was a blow he would take a long time to recover from. That she was in love with someone else, he could accept, if grudgingly, but *this* . . . His harmless little pretence was as inconsequential as a French farce compared with hers.

"Go to bed, Nicola," he said wearily. "I don't think we have anything further to say to each other. Thank you for the tea. I should like to drink it before it gets cold."

Nicola took one last, long look at him. "Magnus." Couldn't he see that she truly loved him, that she was sorry, that...? But even if he could, it would make no difference if he didn't really care for her. She was crazy even to have hoped that he did. He'd only known her for a few days, and even then not the real Nicola Sharman, only the sham. Just because she'd fallen in love with him...

"Good night, Nicola," he said firmly. "And goodbye. I daresay I shan't see you in the morning."

Nicola battled with an intense desire to fling herself into his arms in one last desperate bid to rekindle the infatuation she knew he'd had for her and turn it into forgiveness and love. His expression was too grim, too uncompromising, however, so instead she turned and left the room.

By morning, Nicola was dry-eyed and calm. Her emotions were at last tightly, if precariously, under control, as she prepared to leave once more. If only she could have got away yesterday before he'd seen her! If only she hadn't let an old woman's ramblings influence her.

Dark shadows under her eyes and a slight puffiness of her lids were telltale signs of the long, tortured night she'd spent. If this was what falling in love did to one, she thought, giving her reflection a grim smile, then she was never going to fall in love again. There wasn't much fear of that, she mused wistfully. Where would she find another man like Angus—Magnus? It was so hard to think of him as Magnus, and she had to keep mentally pinching herself to believe it was true and that he was the man she'd come to interview, and that the real Angus was brawny, red-haired and extroverted, and not in the least like Magnus.

Since he had clearly stated he wished to avoid her this morning, no doubt he would have gone out as usual after making himself an early-morning cup of tea. She paused at the thought. Maybe now that Angus was back, he wouldn't need to and would remain in his room until he was sure she had left. He might even watch covertly for her departure, to make sure she had gone before he emerged.

She crossed to the window and looked out. The sun was near to rising and the mountains were bathed in a golden glow. There was still snow on the higher slopes, but lower down there were patches of earth showing through, and the yard this morning was a quagmire of melted snow. As she watched, small avalanches slid off tree branches and exploded in a flurry of flakes as they hit the ground. Suddenly aware that she was wasting time, Nicola dragged herself from the scene, made a last check of the room to be sure she had left nothing behind, and then carried her luggage down to the hall.

She wasn't hungry, but she was dying for a cup of tea and decided she might as well see if Magnus had made the usual pot and left some for her. Also, if the pot was there under its woollen cosy, she would know he had gone out as usual, and that meant he wouldn't come back for at least another hour. He'd have to get his own breakfast this morning. Morag would no doubt be along later, in time for lunch.

Nicola left her luggage by the back door and returned to the kitchen. If there was no teapot on the table, that meant Magnus wasn't up yet, and she must vanish as quietly and quickly as she could in case he suddenly appeared. She could stop somewhere on the road south for breakfast.

As she pushed the door open, the corner of the kitchen table came into view first and the teapot was there, as usual. Nicola heaved a small sigh of relief and opened the door wide.

Then she gasped. Magnus was standing by the window, a cup and saucer in his hand. He turned round as he heard her come in, and Nicola wanted to run but couldn't. "I—I didn't expect you to be here," she muttered, pointing vaguely at the teapot.

He looked at her steadily. "I was waiting for you. I was watching the garages in case you didn't stop for breakfast."

"I only want a cup of tea. You usually leave one in the pot." Why had he waited to see her?

Unexpectedly a faint smile curled around his mouth, softening it. "Nicola, there's something I want to say to you."

The deep melodious voice made the bands on her heart tighten. Would she ever stop hearing it in her mind? She shook her head. "Don't. Please. You said we had nothing more to say to each other. Can't we leave it at that? It's too painful for both of us. I'll be going...." She turned back to the still-open door. "Goodbye, Magnus."

He moved swiftly, and as he had done once before, stationed himself between her and the door and slammed it shut with his foot. "No," he said with quiet determination. "You're not going."

Nicola was bewildered. "What? Magnus, please, I—I can't stand much more."

He looked down into her eyes regretfully. "I know, and I'm sorry. Nicola." Slowly he opened his arms and held them out to her. His plea was simple, unmistakable. "Nicola, forgive me. Last night I was so angry and humiliated at having been duped, I couldn't think straight. I could only see the deception. I let my anger and disappointment override all my other feelings. I was very unjust to you. After all, I had deceived you, too."

Nicola felt her mind going numb, but her body seemed to move of its own volition, forward into his waiting arms. She felt them close about her with such a feeling of disbelief that she was sure she must be dreaming.

But Magnus's lips on hers were no dream, nor was the surge of love that welled up in her at his touch. He held her tightly and his embrace left her in no doubt as to his feelings. And her own seemed to take flight, as though a tightly coiled spring had been released.

At last, both breathless and flushed, they drew apart, although Magnus kept his arms loosely about her, as if to prevent her sudden escape. He looked deeply into her eyes. "Nicola, I meant it when I said I loved you. Everything else was lies, because I have as much pride as anyone. Last night I thought you had strangled that love, but I was wrong. It was stronger than anything I've ever felt before, and I knew I couldn't let you go without discovering if you did have deeper feelings for me then I supposed." He smiled wryly. "I think you just proved what I wanted you to."

Nicola moved close to him, linking her arms around his waist and laying her cheek against his broad chest. "Angus—sorry, Magnus. I just can't get used to you having another name."

"You will. Just one extra letter, that's all, my darling."

"Magnus," she repeated. "It's a very nice name."

"Not as nice as Nicola."

She lifted her face to smile at him, and he touched his lips to her long silky lashes, trailed kissed down her nose and finally brought his mouth hungrily to hers again. She felt his chest heave in a deep, contented sigh as he lifted his head and murmured, "I would never have believed it could happen—a sneaky little reporter, devastating my life, conquering my heart...."

"Last night you even thought I was after your title," Nicola reminded him drily.

"Aren't you?" He was laughing at her slyly. "Aren't you colonials mad about titles?"

"We're not colonials!" she retorted indignantly. "And you can give up your title, for all I care."

He looked at her intently for a moment. "Yes, I believe you mean that. I never used it in my work, anyway. And thanks to you, I hope soon to return to filmmaking."

"Magnus!" His name came more easily already. "You mean that?"

He hugged her against his side. "Why don't we have breakfast and talk a few things over? Angus can cope with the estate. He's got Jock, and some of the hands will come today. We're in no hurry."

"Morag will be arriving this morning," Nicola reminded him.

"Not for an hour or so. So let's straighten a few things out, shall we?"

As Nicola prepared breakfast, they talked, and their eyes were never long away from each other, and Magnus reached out often to touch her whenever she was close enough to where he sat. Strangely, there wasn't as much to say as Nicola had first imagined there would be. She told him the whole truth about her assignment, about Hugh, and why she intended to resign. She even delved into her handbag and produced the letter she had written last night and intended to post that morning.

He pushed it back across the table to her. "I only need your word, Nicola." He turned the envelope over a couple of times, and then grinned at her. "In any case, it's a bit thin for an article...."

"I could never have written the sort of story Hugh and Maynah would want," she said. "Oh, Magnus, it must have been terrible for you. First the tragedy and then to be hounded."

"It was," he admitted. "But I was a fool to let my anger and bitterness last for fifteen years." He smiled at her. "Or perhaps it was just as well I did. Perhaps it all had to happen, so that you could come along and show me how stupid I was, just mouldering away at Craigmoor." He stroked her hair lovingly.

"You really mean you'll go back to filmmaking?" she prompted, recalling his earlier remark.

"I hope so. You're right, it's a shame to waste one's talent, and you wouldn't believe the times I've hauled my cameras out of the cupboard and agonised over them, then put them away because I'd vowed never to enter that world, or the public eye, again. But I'm not going to shoot the same kind of films, Nicola. It began to come to me that day on the mountain when you were photographing the eagles. All at once I realised that you had hit on what I wanted to do. I want to make documentaries. Wildlife films. I want to show the world how important it is for our own survival that we share the earth with its other inhabitants." He stopped, laughing apologetically. "This is hardly the time to mount a soapbox. But... will you help me, Nicola? Will you write the commentaries for me? Can we do this together?"

"It sounds wonderful," she said, her heart nearly bursting.

He said reflectively, "It will be so different with you. You're not like Jacynth, not in any way. We were a team in a sense, because I always shot her films; but we didn't share. Jacynth was very insecure. To be happy, she always had to be centre stage, surrounded by people who adored her. She didn't know about the quiet ways of love, the unspoken words, the way people who truly care for each other take each other for granted." He stopped and smiled apologetically. "Why am I talking about her when all I'm thinking about is you?"

"She was a part of you once," Nicola said slowly. "She changed your life. I don't mind you talking about her. I'm not jealous. Now eat your porridge."

He pulled her down onto his lap. "Not jealous, but bossy." He kissed her very tenderly. "Nicola, I'm so happy this morning. I haven't been so happy for a long, long time, if ever." He laughed suddenly. "Old Mairi was right, as usual, though for a while I was sure she must have been mistaken."

"She saw things for you?" Nicola asked in surprise. "Recently?"

He nodded. "Yes, indeed. Extraordinary things. She told me she had seen a young woman with brown hair and beautiful green eyes enter my house who could alter my future if I allowed it. She told me there were obstacles and quarrels and misunderstandings. She even saw us with the eagles and on Skye."

"So you were fulfilling her prophecy deliberately when you took me there?" Nicola exclaimed.

"Not deliberately. But whatever I thought of doing, I suddenly realised it was something she had seen. She rang me up that day just before you came to tell me she'd had an important vision, and Old Mairi doesn't ride her bike several miles out of her way to make a phone call unless it's urgent. Even though she'd long ago seen tragedy with Jacynth, I was still sceptical, but less so when, not very long afterwards, I caught you trespassing in the woods."

"She told you I was a journalist?"

"No. Maybe she saw it, maybe she didn't. People who have the sight sometimes are careful how much they reveal. I think now she probably saw Jacynth's death, but all she could do was warn me that the marriage would end in tragedy. I didn't listen. But perhaps I couldn't have prevented it, anyway. Jacynth's destiny was partly her own making, as all our destinies are. This time, though, Old Mairi seemed certain that the woman entering my house would bring happiness. Perhaps if she'd told me who you were, I wouldn't have heeded anything else she'd said. Old Mairi is wiser than we know.''

Nicola said, ''When I met her on the road and asked the way, she went into a kind of trance and spoke about a woman finding her destiny, and other things I couldn't catch because of her accent, except that she said the woman was from across the sea, and that she would never return.''

''So it was when she met you that day that she had her vision. I did wonder, but you didn't say.''

''I thought I was silly to take notice of her, but she frightened me a little. I was trying not to be superstitious.''

''Perhaps it was just as well you didn't understand everything she said,'' Magnus went on gently. ''You will return, Nicola. To Australia. Of course you will, but not permanently.'' He twisted a lock of her hair. ''We'll have a honeymoon in Australia and visit your father and anyone else you want to see. What about some sunshine on the Great Barrier Reef? You'll be needing it after all this unpredictable Scottish weather.''

''It sounds too wonderful to be true.''

''I know,'' Magnus said softly, looking gravely at her. ''I thought I would never have the courage to fall in love again. I thought I could never ask a woman to marry me with such a terrible doubt hanging over my past. Nicola, are you sure? You know what was said about me?''

She was amazed that he could ask her that now, but her understanding of his self-doubt made her forgive. ''Magnus, I am going to say this once more, and I don't ever want to be asked to say it again. Yes, I am sure. I know you had nothing to do with your wife's death.''

"How can you be so sure?"

"You told me the truth and I believe you."

The grey eyes showed he still needed convincing. "How do you know it's the truth?"

Nicola laid her head on his shoulder. Gently, she said, "Magnus, I don't. But it doesn't matter. Because I love you. That's all that matters now. You, me, Craigmoor, the future—Now will you stop pestering me and believe me?"

He turned her chin until he could kiss her. "I believe you, my darling lassie." He hadn't quite finished with doubting her, however. "Will you like living here?" he asked anxiously. "It's very isolated."

"I would like living on the moon if you were there," she answered, tugging his beard and kissing him. She went on thoughtfully, "I wonder if Old Mairi did see us like this?"

Magnus chuckled. "Maybe she was too embarrassed to say so. Oh, Nicola, I wish *I* could have seen it—then I wouldn't have treated you so unfairly."

"Magnus, when she came to pay her rent, I asked her about her gift and she insisted that everyone has the sight, but few realise it. She said we can see our futures by looking at the present, that the future is just the result of our actions now. She seemed to suggest that fate wasn't inflexible, that even what was seen could be changed if we wanted it to be, or prevented if we weren't foolish."

"Was that why you came and confessed to me last night?" Magnus said.

Nicola smiled. "When you stopped me from leaving yesterday, I felt it was fate giving me an opportunity to do something about my own destiny. I knew I had to take a gamble and confess." She sighed. "I tried to believe that you would forgive me and that if you did, it would prove you really loved me. You see, I had to know. I couldn't go through life wondering if I could have changed things by taking a chance."

"When I considered it calmly, I knew it had to be something like that." Magnus brought her fingers to his lips in a strangely formal gesture. "For you to have swallowed your pride, there had to be a very good reason. You could have gone and I would never have known the truth. You could have written a story for your magazine and laughed about me with your friends. But at first when you confessed, I was too shocked, too angry to believe your real motives. It took a long night of soul-searching to convince me that if I let you go this morning, I would be letting go the only happiness I could expect in the future."

"We have to take some responsibility for ourselves," Nicola said soberly. "We mustn't accept everything as preordained and inescapable. We can, of our own free will, change our destiny if we wish."

"We change each other," Magnus said reflectively, rubbing his fingertips across hers and sending small shocks through her. "You've certainly changed me. You brought me back to life, Nicola, made me realise that I hadn't lost the capacity to love, and that there was a future with broader horizons than just the boundaries of Craigmoor."

Nicola shook her head. "I only made you see your real self, Magnus, just as you made me see myself. We were both masquerading in another way, I suppose, the way people often do. I was never cut out to be a journalist— not the *Private Lives* kind, anyway—but I somehow got stuck with it. I thought I had to turn myself into a hard-bitten, aggressive reporter in order to be successful. Hugh was always telling me, and Maynah was too, that the story must come first. I had to fall in love with my toughest interviewee, even though I didn't know who he was, to realise that probing people's private lives wasn't what I wanted to do, and that I certainly didn't want to cheat and lie to get stories from difficult subjects. When I realised that because of doing just that, I was going to lose the only real love I'd ever know, I knew I had to resign. Old Mairi said we were earthbound, but that we could fly like eagles if we wanted to. I decided to try and fly."

"For which I am very glad," he murmured, "because now we'll fly together. Together always, my darling Nicola."

She stroked his beard and lightly kissed his lips again. "Lady Catriona intends to make you shave your beard off."

"The minx! Never. Not for her, but for you, my darling, if you want me to...."

"No. I might fall out of love with you if you did. You wouldn't be the same person."

"You don't think I'm still hiding behind it, that I should shed it along with the rest of the past?"

Nicola regarded him thoughtfully. "Only if you feel it's a symbol to you and you feel it's necessary to get rid of it for your peace of mind. But I think you can shake off the past without shaving your beard, and I like it."

"Whatever you wish for, it shall be yours," he said, rubbing her chin gently with the springy dark hairs on his, and managing to brush her lips with his as he did so.

"Can I have one more wish, then?" she murmured.

"Anything, my love."

"Magnus, will you wear a kilt for our wedding? I think you'd look very handsome in a kilt."

Magnus gave a roar of laughter and hugged her tightly. "I'll wear a kilt every day if it makes you love me more."

"Nothing could do that. Oh, Magnus, I'm so happy."

"Not as happy as I am," he said softly, his lips still close to hers.

"Magnus," murmured Nicola as his kiss promised to grow more demanding, "our porridge is getting cold, and you hate cold porridge, remember?"

He drew back in mock alarm. "Ugh! You're right." And then instead of pushing her off his lap, he gathered her tightly into his arms and said huskily, "To hell with the porridge! We can heat it up and have it for—" He paused and looked with intense longing and all the love she could hope for into her shining eyes, then said gravely, "Lunch!"

"Magnus!" Nicola dissolved into laughter, snuggled close in his arms, and was about to remind him that Morag would be arriving at any time, but his mouth on hers prevented speech. In any case, whenever Magnus kissed her, she always forgot what she had meant to say.

* * * * *

Next Month's Romances

Each month you can choose from a wide variety of romance with Mills & Boon. Below are the new titles to look out for next month, why not ask either Mills & Boon Reader Service or your Newsagent to reserve you a copy of the titles you want to buy – just tick the titles you would like and either post to Reader Service or take it to any Newsagent and ask them to order your books.

Please save me the following titles: **Please tick** | ✓

PASSION'S MISTRESS	Helen Bianchin	
THE UPSTAIRS LOVER	Emma Darcy	
BODY AND SOUL	Charlotte Lamb	
WAITING FOR DEBORAH	Betty Neels	
WILDFIRE	Sandra Field	
IN NAME ONLY	Diana Hamilton	
AN IMPORTED WIFE	Rosalie Ash	
BLAMELESS DESIRE	Jenny Cartwright	
MASTER OF DESTINY	Sally Heywood	
DANCE TO THE DEVIL'S TUNE	Lucy Keane	
LIVING FOR LOVE	Barbara McMahon	
DARK AVENGER	Alex Ryder	
WHEN STRANGERS MEET	Shirley Kemp	
PAST IMPERFECT	Kristy McCallum	
JACINTH	Laurey Bright	
HEIR TO GLENGYLE	Miriam Macgregor	

If you would like to order these books in addition to your regular subscription from Mills & Boon Reader Service please send £1.90 per title to: Mills & Boon Reader Service, Freepost, P.O. Box 236, Croydon, Surrey, CR9 9EL, quote your Subscriber No:.................................. (If applicable) and complete the name and address details below. Alternatively, these books are available from many local Newsagents including W H Smith, J Menzies, Martins and other paperback stockists from 13 May 1994.

Name:..

Address:...

....Post Code:...........................

To Retailer: If you would like to stock M&B books please contact your regular book/magazine wholesaler for details.

You may be mailed with offers from other reputable companies as a result of this application.
If you would rather not take advantage of these opportunities please tick box ☐

FREE BOOK · OFFER

HEARTS OF FIRE

By Miranda Lee

HEARTS OF FIRE by Miranda Lee is a totally compelling six-part saga set in Australia's glamorous but cut-throat world of gem dealing.

Discover the passion, scandal, sin and finally the hope that exists between two fabulously rich families. You'll be hooked from the very first page...

Each of the six novels in this series features a gripping romance. And the first title **SEDUCTION AND SACRIFICE** can be yours absolutely FREE! You can also reserve the remaining five novels in this exciting series from Reader Service, delivered to your door for £2.50 each. And remember postage and packing is FREE!

MILLS & BOON READER SERVICE, FREEPOST, P.O. BOX 236, CROYDON CR9 9EL. TEL: 081-684 2141

YES! Please send me my FREE book (part 1 in the Hearts of Fire series) and reserve me a subscription for the remaining 5 books in the series. I understand that you will send me one book each month and invoice me £2.50 each month.

NO STAMP NEEDED

MILLS & BOON READER SERVICE, FREEPOST, P.O. BOX 236, CROYDON CR9 9EL. TEL: 081-684 2141

Ms/Mrs/Miss/Mr: _____ EPHOF

Address _____

_____

_____ Postcode _____

Offer expires 31st. August 1994. One per household. The right is reserved to refuse an application and change the terms of this offer. Offer applies to U.K. and Eire only. Readers overseas please send for details. Southern Africa write to : IBS Private Bag X3010, Randburg 2125. You may be mailed with offers from other reputable companies as a result of this application. If you would prefer not to receive such offers please tick box. ☐